THE BRAIN WORKS

Published by Sellers Publishing, Inc.
Copyright © 2012 Sellers Publishing, Inc
Text copyright © 2012 TriviaTex
All rights reserved.

Sellers Publishing, Inc.
161 John Roberts Road, South Portland, Maine 04106
Visit our Web site: www.sellerspublishing.com
E-mail: rsp@rsvp.com

ISBN 13: 978-1-4162-0687-3

Designed by George Corsillo/Design Monsters

10 9 8 7 6 5 4 3 2 1

Printed and bound in the United States of America.

BRAIN WORKS

The Movie Maniac's ULTIMATE PUZZLE and TRIVIA Book

TriviaTex

SELLERS
PUBLISHING

THE BRAIN WORKS

The Movie Maniac's Ultimate Puzzle and Trivia Book is the Red Carpet guide to the world of Hollywood. With more trivia puzzles than Oscar night nominations, this is the top puzzler on actors, directors, and movie titles. The book features 275 puzzles presented in 14 themed variations from Remake My Day to Script Tease and Movie Teasers to The Envelope, Please. Test your film knowledge and have some fun along the way.

- Fourteen styles of movie triva puzzles to challenge all levels of players

- Be prepared for some serious mental gymnastics!

- 275 puzzles with solutions in the back of the book

- Easy-to-carry around size

The Movie Maniac's
ULTIMATE PUZZLE
and TRIVIA Book

Match Game

Match each actor with the film in which he played the president of the United States.

1. Bill Pullman	A. "Air Force One"
2. Billy Bob Thornton	B. "The American President"
3. Chris Rock	C. "Dave"
4. Harrison Ford	D. "Deep Impact"
5. John Travolta	E. "Dr. Strangelove"
6. Kevin Kline	F. "Head of State"
7. Michael Douglas	G. "Independence Day"
8. Morgan Freeman	H. "Love Actually"
9. Stephen Colbert	I. "Monsters vs. Aliens"
10. Peter Sellers	J. "Primary Colors"

SOLUTIONS: PAGE 281

Script Tease

Fill in the word missing from each movie quote, then rearrange the first letters of the filled-in words to spell a 5-letter movie title.

1. "The _____ in Spain falls mainly on the plain." —**"MY FAIR LADY"**

2. "I'm as mad as hell, and I'm not going to take this _____!" —**"NETWORK"**

3. "Play it, Sam. Play 'As Time _____ By.'" —**"CASABLANCA"**

4. "_____, my dear, I don't give a damn." —**"GONE WITH THE WIND"**

5. "Snap _____ of it!" —**"MOONSTRUCK"**

Movie Title: ☐☐☐☐☐

SOLUTIONS: PAGE 281

Remake My Day

Same title, different cast.
Can you identify the movie?

ORIGINAL CAST

STEVE McQUEEN
FAYE DUNAWAY

REMAKE CAST

PIERCE BROSNAN
RENE RUSSO

Hollywood Connections

The name is spelled in the grid by starting on the dot of the first letter and drawing a line from letter one to letter two, letter two to letter three, and so on, until the entire answer is spelled out.

Can you determine the answer?

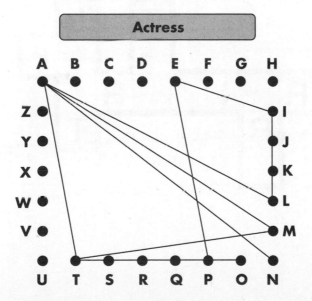

Actress

Film Strips

The crisscross below contains all of the words from a popular movie title. Can you reconstruct the words and discover the title?

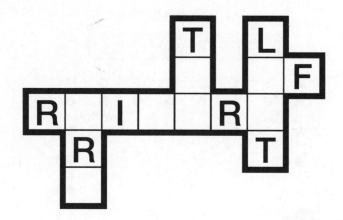

SOLUTIONS: PAGE 281

Movie-Tac-Toe

Which row, column, or diagonal in the grid contains titles of three films directed by Martin Scorsese?

Correct ✓

E.T.	GANGS OF NEW YORK	THE DEPARTED
GOOD-FELLAS	THE SHINING	TAXI DRIVER
THE AVIATOR	AVATAR	SHUTTER ISLAND

SOLUTIONS: PAGE 281

11

Quick Quiz

Though he was nominated five times, which director never won a Best Director Oscar?

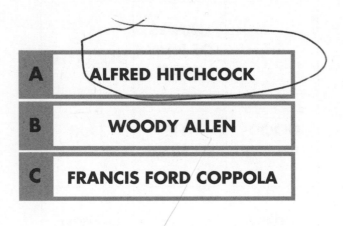

A ALFRED HITCHCOCK

B WOODY ALLEN

C FRANCIS FORD COPPOLA

Movie Teaser

Rearrange the letters in the words below to spell the 2-word title of a popular 2003 movie.

INFO MENDING

Movie-Tac-Toe

Which row, column, or diagonal in the grid contains titles of James Bond movies starring Sean Connery?

DIE ANOTHER DAY	YOU ONLY LIVE TWICE	A VIEW TO A KILL
THE SPY WHO LOVED ME	DR. NO	LIVE AND LET DIE
CASINO ROYALE	FROM RUSSIA WITH LOVE	DIAMONDS ARE FOREVER

SOLUTIONS: PAGE 281

Fiction or non-?

True or False?

Actor Henry Fonda
never won a
Best Actor Oscar.

SOLUTIONS: PAGE 281

Movie Lines

Write a famous name into the blanks to form a chain of three overlapping names reading down. For example, given ELTON _____ _____ NEWTON, you'd write JOHN WAYNE in the blanks to form ELTON JOHN, JOHN WAYNE, and WAYNE NEWTON.

STOCKARD

_____

_____

O'NEAL

The List

Five of the following ten movies feature Harrison Ford. Can you pick them out?

_____ "Footloose"

_____ "In the Line of Fire"

_____ "Apocalypse Now"

_____ "The Rookie"

_____ "The Fugitive"

_____ "Six Days Seven Nights"

_____ "Shall We Dance"

✓ "Patriot Games"

_____ "Pretty Woman"

_____ "Air Force One"

SOLUTIONS: PAGE 281

Order Please

Put these actresses in order by the number of Best Actress nominations they've received, starting with the most.

1 | **FAYE DUNAWAY**

2 | **KATHARINE HEPBURN**

3 | **GLENN CLOSE**

4 | **KATE WINSLET**

5 | **ELIZABETH TAYLOR**

SOLUTIONS: PAGE 281

What's My Line?

Even before films were in color, films had colors in their titles. Place a color in each blank to complete the movie title.

1. "A Clockwork _Orange_"
2. "_Yellow_ Submarine"
3. "Pretty in _Pink_"
4. "Meet Joe _green_"
5. "How _____ Was My Valley"
6. "The _blue_ Lagoon"
7. "_____ Nights"
8. "The Unsinkable Molly _____"
9. "The Man With One _red_ Shoe"

SOLUTIONS: PAGE 281

19

Match Game

Match each U.S. landmark to the film in which it is featured prominently.

1. Brooklyn Bridge
2. Empire State Building
3. Lincoln Memorial
4. Golden Gate Bridge
5. Grand Canyon
6. Mount Rushmore
7. Sears Tower
8. Statue of Liberty

A. "An Affair to Remember"
B. "A View to Kill"
C. "Ferris Bueller's Day Off"
D. "Forrest Gump"
E. "North by Northwest"
F. "Planet of the Apes"
G. "Saturday Night Fever"
H. "Vacation"

Script Tease

Fill in the word missing from each movie quote, then rearrange the first letters of the filled-in words to spell a 5-letter movie title.

1. "I'm going to make him an offer he can't _refuse_." —**"THE GODFATHER"**

2. "_____, my dear Watson."
   —**"SHERLOCK HOLMES"**

3. "Love means never having to say you're _____." —**"LOVE STORY"**

4. "Toto, I've got a feeling we're not in _Kansas_ anymore." —**"THE WIZARD OF OZ"**

5. "E.T., phone _home_."
   —**"E.T. THE EXTRA-TERRESTRIAL"**

Movie Title: ☐ ☐ ☐ ☐ ☐

SOLUTIONS: PAGE 281

Remake My Day

Same title, different cast.
Can you identify the movie?

ORIGINAL CAST

JOHN WAYNE
KIM DARBY

REMAKE CAST

JEFF BRIDGES
HAILEE STEINFELD

SOLUTIONS: PAGE 281

Hollywood Connections

The name is spelled in the grid by starting on the dot of the first letter and drawing a line from letter one to letter two, letter two to letter three, and so on, until the entire answer is spelled out.

Can you determine the answer?

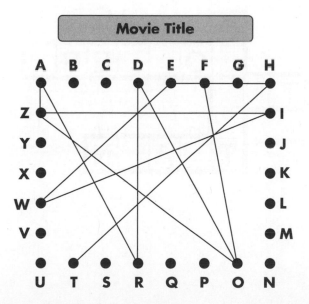

Movie Title

```
A   B   C   D   E   F   G   H
Z                           I
Y                           J
X                           K
W                           L
V                           M
U   T   S   R   Q   P   O   N
```

Film Strips

The crisscross below contains all of the words from a popular movie title. Can you reconstruct the words and discover the title?

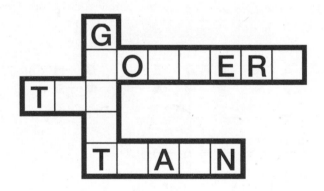

SOLUTIONS: PAGE 281

Movie-Tac-Toe

Which row, column, or diagonal in the grid contains titles of three Tom Cruise films?

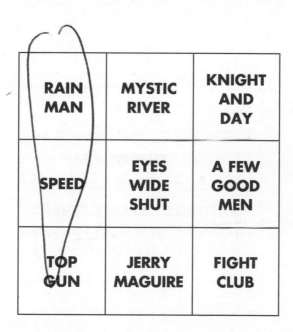

RAIN MAN	MYSTIC RIVER	KNIGHT AND DAY
SPEED	EYES WIDE SHUT	A FEW GOOD MEN
TOP GUN	JERRY MAGUIRE	FIGHT CLUB

Quick Quiz

With over 17 million albums sold, what is the best-selling movie soundtrack of all time?

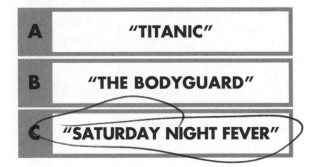

A	"TITANIC"
B	"THE BODYGUARD"
C	"SATURDAY NIGHT FEVER"

SOLUTIONS: PAGE 281

Movie Teaser

Rearrange the letters in the words below to spell the 2-word title of a popular 1989 movie.

| NASTY HAYING |

The Envelope, Please

The envelope below contains information about a prizewinning actor, movie, or both. All clues have been replaced with initials. Using the clues shown, can you determine what each set of initials stands for?

BEST DIRECTOR WINNER:

C.E. *for*
"M.D.B."

Fiction or non-?

True or False?

> James Dean had major roles in only three films before he passed away in 1955.

Quick Quiz

Which actor was born Ramon Estevez?

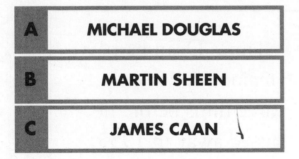

A	MICHAEL DOUGLAS
B	MARTIN SHEEN
C	JAMES CAAN

SOLUTIONS: PAGE 281

The List

Actress Frances McDormand is married to director Joel Coen. Below, check off the 5 Coen brothers films that feature Frances McDormand.

_____ "Barton Fink"

_____ "The Big Lebowski"

_____ "Blood Simple"

_____ "Burn After Reading"

_____ "Fargo"

_____ "The Man Who Wasn't There"

_____ "No Country for Old Men"

_____ "O Brother, Where Art Thou?"

_____ "Raising Arizona"

_____ "True Grit"

SOLUTIONS: PAGE 281

Order Please

Put these Pixar films in order of their release, starting with the earliest.

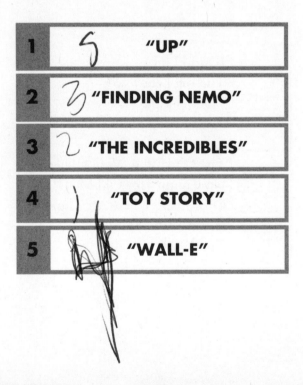

1	"UP"
2	"FINDING NEMO"
3	"THE INCREDIBLES"
4	"TOY STORY"
5	"WALL-E"

SOLUTIONS: PAGE 281

Movie-Tac-Toe

Which row, column, or diagonal in the grid contains three Pixar film titles?

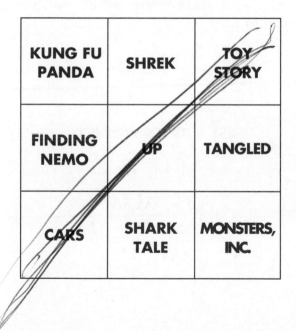

KUNG FU PANDA	SHREK	TOY STORY
FINDING NEMO	UP	TANGLED
CARS	SHARK TALE	MONSTERS, INC.

SOLUTIONS: PAGE 281

The Envelope, Please

The envelope below contains information about a prizewinning actor, movie, or both. All clues have been replaced with initials. Using the clues shown, can you determine what each set of initials stands for?

BEST ACTRESS WINNER:

H.H. *in*
"A.G.A.I.G."

SOLUTIONS: PAGE 281

Film Strips

The crisscross below contains all of the words from a popular movie title. Can you reconstruct the words and discover the title?

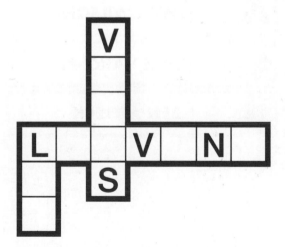

Quick Quiz

In 2006, Jennifer Aniston broke up with what co-star of "The Break-Up"?

A	**OWEN WILSON**
B	**VINCE VAUGHN**
C	**BEN AFFLECK**

Hollywood Connections

The name is spelled in the grid by starting on the dot of the first letter and drawing a line from letter one to letter two, letter two to letter three, and so on, until the entire answer is spelled out.

Can you determine the answer?

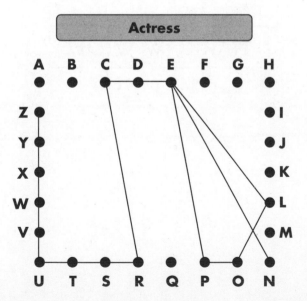

Actress

SOLUTIONS: PAGE 282

Movie Teaser

Rearrange the letters in the words below to spell the 2-word title of a popular 1954 movie.

NARROW WIDE

SOLUTIONS: PAGE 282

Film Strips

The crisscross below contains all of the words from a popular movie title. Can you reconstruct the words and discover the title?

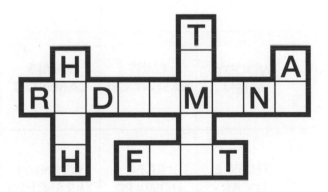

SOLUTIONS: PAGE 282

Movie-Tac-Toe

Which row, column, or diagonal in the grid contains three Best Director winners?

DAVID LYNCH	**FRANK CAPRA**	**ALFRED HITCHCOCK**
WOODY ALLEN	**CLINT EASTWOOD**	**JAMES CAMERON**
GEORGE LUCAS	**RON HOWARD**	**QUENTIN TARANTINO**

SOLUTIONS: PAGE 282

Movie Teaser

Rearrange the letters in the words below to spell the 2-word title of a popular 1957 movie.

PALE POTENCY

SOLUTIONS: PAGE 282

41

The Envelope, Please

The envelope below contains information about a prizewinning actor, movie, or both. All clues have been replaced with initials. Using the clues shown, can you determine what each set of initials stands for?

BEST ACTRESS WINNER:

S.S. *in*

"C.M.D."

Movie Teaser

Rearrange the letters in the words below to spell the 2-word title of a popular 1990 movie.

TEMPT NORWAY

SOLUTIONS: PAGE 282

Film Strips

The crisscross below contains all of the words from a popular movie title. Can you reconstruct the words and discover the title?

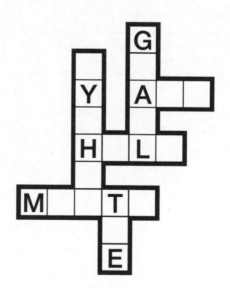

Hollywood Connections

The name is spelled in the grid by starting on the dot of the first letter and drawing a line from letter one to letter two, letter two to letter three, and so on, until the entire answer is spelled out.

Can you determine the answer?

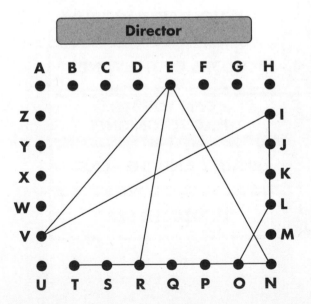

Director

Order Please

Put these songs from Disney films in the order they won Best Original Song, starting with the earliest.

1 "A WHOLE NEW WORLD"

2 "COLORS OF THE WIND"

3 "CAN YOU FEEL THE LOVE TONIGHT"

4 "BEAUTY AND THE BEAST"

5 "UNDER THE SEA"

SOLUTIONS: PAGE 282

Quick Quiz

In 1969, two Best Actress Oscars were awarded: one to Katharine Hepburn for "The Lion in Winter," and one to what actress who received exactly the same number of votes as Ms. Hepburn?

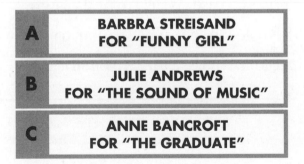

A   BARBRA STREISAND FOR "FUNNY GIRL"

B   JULIE ANDREWS FOR "THE SOUND OF MUSIC"

C   ANNE BANCROFT FOR "THE GRADUATE"

SOLUTIONS: PAGE 282

Fiction or non-?

True or False?

The lead in "Salt" was intended for Tom Cruise, who turned down the role since it was similar to his role in "Mission: Impossible."

SOLUTIONS: PAGE 282

Movie-Tac-Toe

Which row, column, or diagonal in the grid contains three films released in the 1980s?

JAWS	BACK TO THE FUTURE	E.T.
BEVERLY HILLS COP	STAR WARS	DIRTY DANCING
SATURDAY NIGHT FEVER	FLASH-DANCE	THE KARATE KID

SOLUTIONS: PAGE 282

Quick Quiz

In her kitchen, Glenn Close has the knife she used during the filming of what movie?

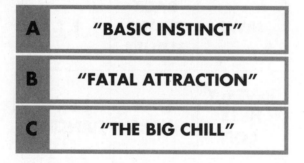

A   "BASIC INSTINCT"

B   "FATAL ATTRACTION"

C   "THE BIG CHILL"

SOLUTIONS: PAGE 282

Fiction or non-?

True or False?

> Liza Minnelli is the
> daughter of
> screen legend
> Joan Crawford.

Film Strips

The crisscross below contains all of the words from a popular movie title. Can you reconstruct the words and discover the title?

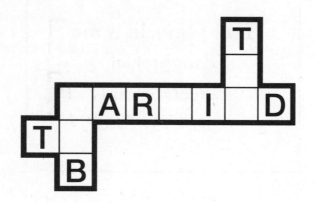

SOLUTIONS: PAGE 282

Order Please

Put these movies in order of their release, starting with the earliest.

1	"ENDLESS LOVE"
2	"FROM RUSSIA WITH LOVE"
3	"LOVE ME TENDER"
4	"LOVE STORY"
5	"TO SIR, WITH LOVE"

SOLUTIONS: PAGE 282

Movie-Tac-Toe

Which row, column, or diagonal in the grid contains three films starring Kevin Bacon?

ANIMAL HOUSE	A FEW GOOD MEN	BIG
APOLLO 13	SAVING PRIVATE RYAN	FOOT-LOOSE
MYSTIC RIVER	SLEEPERS	MOON-STRUCK

Movie Teaser

Rearrange the letters in the words below to spell the 2-word title of a popular 1979 movie.

$$\boxed{\text{MEAN ROAR}}$$

Quick Quiz

Actor Nicolas Cage was born Nicolas Kim Coppola but changed his name so he wouldn't be associated with the director of what film?

A "TAXI DRIVER"

B "IT'S A WONDERFUL LIFE"

C "APOCALYPSE NOW"

SOLUTIONS: PAGE 282

Film Strips

The crisscross below contains all of the words from a popular movie title. Can you reconstruct the words and discover the title?

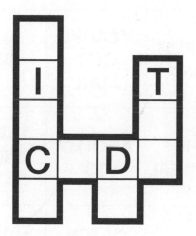

Movie-Tac-Toe

Which row, column, or diagonal in the grid contains three Tom Hanks films released in the 1990s?

FORREST GUMP	YOU'VE GOT MAIL	BIG
THE TERMINAL	APOLLO 13	THE DA VINCI CODE
A LEAGUE OF THEIR OWN	CATCH ME IF YOU CAN	SAVING PRIVATE RYAN

Match Game

Match each actor in the left column with the role he played in the right column.

1. Adrian Brody
2. Arnold Schwarzenegger
3. Dustin Hoffman
4. Kevin Costner
5. Marlon Brando
6. Matt Damon
7. Paul Newman
8. Robert Redford
9. Tim Robbins
10. W. C. Fields

A. "The Bodyguard"
B. "The Bank Dick"
C. "The Godfather"
D. "The Graduate"
E. "The Hustler"
F. "The Informant"
G. "The Natural"
H. "The Pianist"
I. "The Player"
J. "The Terminator"

SOLUTIONS: PAGE 282

Order Please

Time to test your Streep smarts! Put these Meryl Streep movies in order of their release, starting with the earliest.

1	"THE DEVIL WEARS PRADA"
2	"JULIE & JULIA"
3	"OUT OF AFRICA"
4	"SILKWOOD"
5	"SOPHIE'S CHOICE"

SOLUTIONS: PAGE 282

The Envelope, Please

The envelope below contains information about a prizewinning actor, movie, or both. All clues have been replaced with initials. Using the clues shown, can you determine what each set of initials stands for?

BEST ACTOR WINNER:

D.H. *in*
"R.M."

𝒬uick 𝒬uiz

In 2010, Sandra Bullock became the first star to win a Best Actress Oscar and a Worst Actress Razzie in the same year.

The Oscar was for "The Blind Side."

What movie was the Razzie for?

A	**"ALL ABOUT STEVE"**
B	**"THE PROPOSAL"**
C	**"THE LAKE HOUSE"**

SOLUTIONS: PAGE 282

Script Tease

Fill in the word missing from each movie quote, then rearrange the first letters of the filled-in words to spell a 5-letter movie title.

1. "_____ you build it, he will come."
   —**"FIELD OF DREAMS"**

2. "Nobody puts _____ in the corner."
   —**"DIRTY DANCING"**

3. "There's no crying in _____."
   —**"A LEAGUE OF THEIR OWN"**

4. "After all, tomorrow is _____ day."
   —**"GONE WITH THE WIND"**

5. "Show me the _____!"
   —**"JERRY MAGUIRE"**

Movie Title: ☐☐☐☐☐

Film Strips

The crisscross below contains all of the words from a popular movie title. Can you reconstruct the words and discover the title?

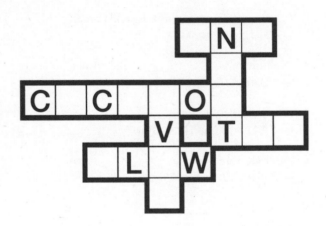

The Envelope, Please

The envelope below contains information about a prizewinning actor, movie, or both. All clues have been replaced with initials. Using the clues shown, can you determine what each set of initials stands for?

BEST DIRECTOR WINNER:

J. & E.C. *for*
"N.C.F.O.M."

SOLUTIONS: PAGE 282

Movie-Tac-Toe

Which row, column, or diagonal in the grid contains three TV shows that were based on popular movies?

GILLIGAN'S ISLAND	THE PINK PANTHER	M*A*S*H
CLUELESS	THE ODD COUPLE	THE A-TEAM
BUFFY THE VAMPIRE SLAYER	SEX AND THE CITY	GET SMART

SOLUTIONS: PAGE 283

Movie Teaser

Rearrange the letters in the words below to spell the 2-word title of a popular 1969 movie.

TRITE RUG

Film Strips

The crisscross below contains all of the words from a popular movie title. Can you reconstruct the words and discover the title?

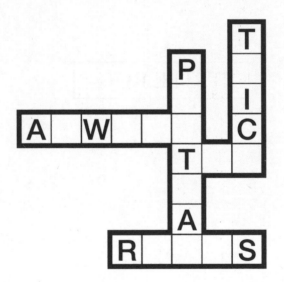

Quick Quiz

In "E.T.," what classic movie theater candy did Elliott use to lure E.T. into his house?

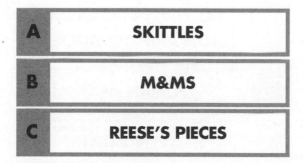

A	SKITTLES
B	M&MS
C	REESE'S PIECES

SOLUTIONS: PAGE 283

Order Please

Put these box office bombs in order of their premiere, starting with the earliest.

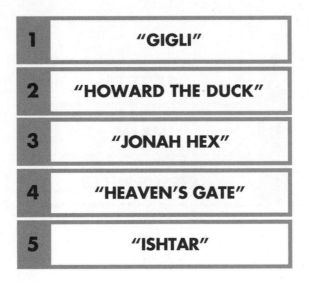

1	"GIGLI"
2	"HOWARD THE DUCK"
3	"JONAH HEX"
4	"HEAVEN'S GATE"
5	"ISHTAR"

SOLUTIONS: PAGE 283

The Envelope, Please

The envelope below contains information about a prizewinning actor, movie, or both. All clues have been replaced with initials. Using the clues shown, can you determine what each set of initials stands for?

BEST ACTOR WINNER:

H.B. *in*

"T.A.Q."

SOLUTIONS: PAGE 283

Quick Quiz

What comedian hosted the Academy Awards
a record 19 times?

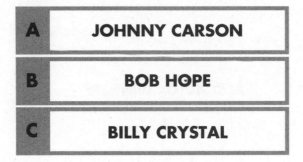

A   JOHNNY CARSON

B   BOB HOPE

C   BILLY CRYSTAL

SOLUTIONS: PAGE 283

Movie-Tac-Toe

Which row, column, or diagonal in the grid contains three films that earned Katharine Hepburn Best Actress awards?

BRINGING UP BABY	**DESK SET**	**GUESS WHO'S COMING TO DINNER**
STAGE DOOR	**MORNING GLORY**	**ON GOLDEN POND**
ADAM'S RIB	**THE AFRICAN QUEEN**	**THE LION IN WINTER**

SOLUTIONS: PAGE 283

Movie Teaser

Rearrange the letters in the words below to spell
the 2-word title of a popular 1970 movie.

SO OVERTLY

Quick Quiz

At the 1942 Academy Awards, the audience booed when what film's name was mentioned?

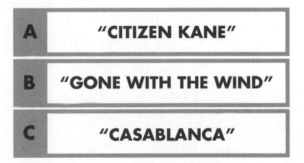

A   "CITIZEN KANE"

B   "GONE WITH THE WIND"

C   "CASABLANCA"

SOLUTIONS: PAGE 283

The List

Five of the following ten films won a Best Picture Oscar.

Can you pick them out?

_____ "Avatar"
_____ "Gladiator"
_____ "Moonstruck"
_____ "Jaws"
_____ "Titanic"
_____ "Rocky"
_____ "Tootsie"
_____ "Braveheart"
_____ "Casablanca"
_____ "Traffic"

SOLUTIONS: PAGE 283

Hollywood Connections

The name is spelled in the grid by starting on the dot of the first letter and drawing a line from letter one to letter two, letter two to letter three, and so on, until the entire answer is spelled out.

Can you determine the answer?

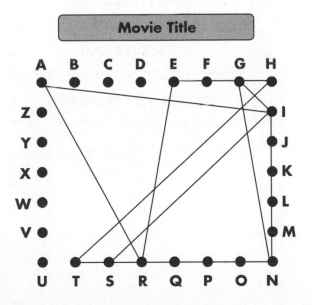

Movie Title

SOLUTIONS: PAGE 283

Quick Quiz

What actor turned down the role of Rhett Butler saying, "'Gone With the Wind' is going to be the biggest flop in Hollywood history?"

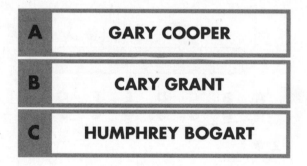

A	**GARY COOPER**
B	**CARY GRANT**
C	**HUMPHREY BOGART**

Movie-Tac-Toe

Which row, column, or diagonal in the grid contains three films that won Best Picture in the 2000s?

MILLION DOLLAR BABY	**CRASH**	**THE DEPARTED**
SLUMDOG MILLIONAIRE	**CAPOTE**	**THE PIANIST**
JUNO	**SHAKES-PEARE IN LOVE**	**AVATAR**

SOLUTIONS: PAGE 283

Quick Quiz

AFI's list of the top 100 songs from American cinema includes three songs from what movie musical?

A	**"GREASE"**
B	**"THE SOUND OF MUSIC"**
C	**"MARY POPPINS"**

SOLUTIONS: PAGE 283

The Envelope, Please

The envelope below contains information about a prizewinning actor, movie, or both. All clues have been replaced with initials. Using the clues shown, can you determine what each set of initials stands for?

BEST ACTOR WINNER:

A.H. *in*
"T.S.O.T.L."

SOLUTIONS: PAGE 283

Film Strips

The crisscross below contains all of the words from a popular movie title. Can you reconstruct the words and discover the title?

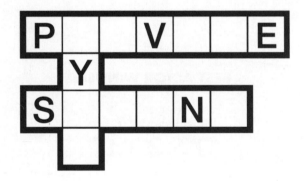

The Envelope, Please

The envelope below contains information about a prizewinning actor, movie, or both. All clues have been replaced with initials. Using the clues shown, can you determine what each set of initials stands for?

BEST PICTURE WINNER:

"C.O.F."

SOLUTIONS: PAGE 283

Order Please

Put these Nora Ephron films in order of their release, starting with the earliest.

1   "MICHAEL"

2   "SILKWOOD"

3   "SLEEPLESS IN SEATTLE"

4   "WHEN HARRY MET SALLY"

5   "YOU'VE GOT MAIL"

SOLUTIONS: PAGE 283

Quick Quiz

While filming "Jaws," Steven Spielberg named the mechanical sharks "Bruce," after whom?

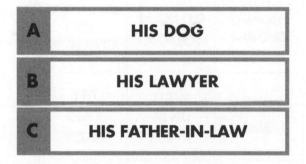

A — HIS DOG

B — HIS LAWYER

C — HIS FATHER-IN-LAW

SOLUTIONS: PAGE 283

Movie-Tac-Toe

Which row, column, or diagonal in the grid contains three films starring Audrey Hepburn?

THE THOMAS CROWN AFFAIR	ROMAN HOLIDAY	BREAKFAST AT TIFFANY'S
FUNNY GIRL	WAIT UNTIL DARK	MY FAIR LADY
CHARADE	MARY POPPINS	NETWORK

SOLUTIONS: PAGE 283

What's My Line?

Here's a quiz for city slickers. Place the name of a U.S. or world city in each blank to complete a film title.

1. "Sleepless in _Seattle_"

2. "Fear and Loathing in _____"

3. "_____ Confidential"

4. "Meet Me in _____"

5. "_LA_ Vice"

6. "The Purple Rose of _____"

7. "Vicky Cristina _____"

8. "3:10 to _____"

SOLUTIONS: PAGE 283

Movie-Tac-Toe

Which row, column, or diagonal in the grid contains three films that won Best Picture in the 1990s?

THE LAST EMPEROR	A BEAUTIFUL MIND	BRAVEHEART
AMADEUS	TITANIC	OUT OF AFRICA
THE ENGLISH PATIENT	DANCES WITH WOLVES	PATTON

SOLUTIONS: PAGE 283

Film Strips

The crisscross below contains all of the words
from a popular movie title. Can you reconstruct
the words and discover the title?

Quick Quiz

Who went from failing a film class and being expelled from N.Y.U. to writing jokes for "The Ed Sullivan Show" and the "Tonight Show" at age 19?

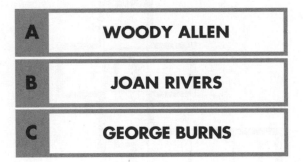

A	WOODY ALLEN
B	JOAN RIVERS
C	GEORGE BURNS

Hollywood Connections

The name is spelled in the grid by starting on the dot of the first letter and drawing a line from letter one to letter two, letter two to letter three, and so on, until the entire answer is spelled out.

Can you determine the answer?

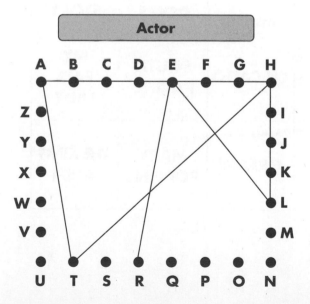

Actor

SOLUTIONS: PAGE 283

91

Movie-Tac-Toe

Which row, column, or diagonal in the grid contains three films based on Rodgers and Hammerstein plays?

THE SOUND OF MUSIC	**GUYS AND DOLLS**	**WEST SIDE STORY**
CHICAGO	**SOUTH PACIFIC**	**MY FAIR LADY**
GREASE	**MARY POPPINS**	**THE KING AND I**

SOLUTIONS: PAGE 283

The Envelope, Please

The envelope below contains information about a prizewinning actor, movie, or both. All clues have been replaced with initials. Using the clues shown, can you determine what each set of initials stands for?

BEST PICTURE WINNER:

"D.W.W."

The Envelope, Please

The envelope below contains information about a prizewinning actor, movie, or both. All clues have been replaced with initials. Using the clues shown, can you determine what each set of initials stands for?

BEST ACTRESS WINNER:

S.M. *in*
"T.O.E."

Movie Teaser

Rearrange the letters in the words below to spell the 2-word title of a popular 1973 movie.

> ## ROMAN POPE

SOLUTIONS: PAGE 283

Match Game

Match the performers in the left column with the James Bond theme songs they sang in the right column.

1. Carly Simon
2. Duran Duran
3. Madonna
4. Nancy Sinatra
5. Paul McCartney & The Wings
6. Rita Coolidge
7. Shirley Bassey
8. Sheena Easton
9. Tom Jones

A. "All Time High"
B. "A View to Kill"
C. "Die Another Day"
D. "For Your Eyes Only"
E. "Goldfinger"
F. "Nobody Does It Better"
G. "Live and Let Die"
H. "Thunderball"
I. "You Only Live Twice"

SOLUTIONS: PAGE 284

Order Please

Put these movies based on SNL sketches in order of their release, starting with the earliest.

1	"THE BLUES BROTHERS"
2	"THE LADIES' MAN"
3	"MacGRUBER"
4	"SUPERSTAR"
5	"WAYNE'S WORLD"

SOLUTIONS: PAGE 284

Remake My Day

Same title, different cast.
Can you identify the movie?

ORIGINAL CAST

WALTER MATTHAU
ROBERT SHAW

REMAKE CAST

DENZEL WASHINGTON
JOHN TRAVOLTA

SOLUTIONS: PAGE 284

Quick Quiz

If today is Take Our Daughters and Sons to Work Day. Which star might actor Jon Voight bring to his movie set?

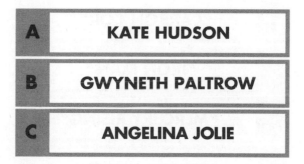

A KATE HUDSON

B GWYNETH PALTROW

C ANGELINA JOLIE

SOLUTIONS: PAGE 284

Order Please

Put these films whose titles feature chemical elements in order of their release, starting with the earliest.

1	"CARBON COPY"
2	"IRON MAN"
3	"MERCURY RISING"
4	"SILVER STREAK"
5	"TIN CUP"

The Envelope, Please

The envelope below contains information about a prizewinning actor, movie, or both. All clues have been replaced with initials. Using the clues shown, can you determine what each set of initials stands for?

BEST ACTRESS WINNER:

V.L. *in*
"A.S.N.D."

Movie-Tac-Toe

Which row, column, or diagonal in the grid contains three films starring Jennifer Lopez?

SHALL WE DANCE	DIRTY DANCING	MR. & MRS. SMITH
THE BACK-UP PLAN	MEAN GIRLS	YOU'VE GOT MAIL
MONSTER -IN-LAW	THE BREAK-UP	GIGLI

SOLUTIONS: PAGE 284

Movie Teaser

Rearrange the letters in the words below to spell the 2-word title of a popular 1998 movie.

CAPPED TIME

Quick Quiz

Which actor made a big splash onto the movie scene by starring in the 1980s films "Big" and "Splash?"

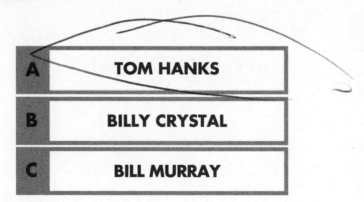

A	TOM HANKS
B	BILLY CRYSTAL
C	BILL MURRAY

SOLUTIONS: PAGE 284

The Envelope, Please

The envelope below contains information about a prizewinning actor, movie, or both. All clues have been replaced with initials. Using the clues shown, can you determine what each set of initials stands for?

BEST ACTOR WINNER:

G.H. *in*
"T.F.C."

SOLUTIONS: PAGE 284

Hollywood Connections

The name is spelled in the grid by starting on the dot of the first letter and drawing a line from letter one to letter two, letter two to letter three, and so on, until the entire answer is spelled out.

Can you determine the answer?

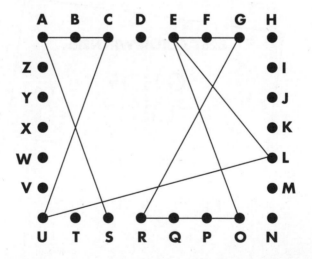

SOLUTIONS: PAGE 284

Quick Quiz

If today is Mother's Day. What actress would Goldie Hawn expect a phone call from?

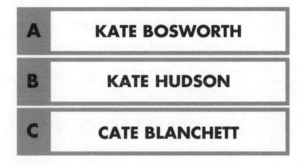

A   **KATE BOSWORTH**

B   **KATE HUDSON**

C   **CATE BLANCHETT**

SOLUTIONS: PAGE 284

Quick Quiz

What movie's opening line is: "Saturday, March 24, 1984. Shermer High School, Shermer, Illinois, 60062. Dear Mr. Vernon..."?

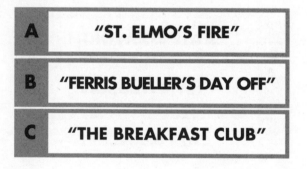

A	**"ST. ELMO'S FIRE"**
B	**"FERRIS BUELLER'S DAY OFF"**
C	**"THE BREAKFAST CLUB"**

SOLUTIONS: PAGE 284

Movie Teaser

Rearrange the letters in the words below to spell the 2-word title of a popular 1987 movie.

CANDID TRYING

Order Please

Put these films with numbers in their titles in order of their release, starting with the earliest.

1	"ONE FLEW OVER THE CUCKOO'S NEST"
2	"THE MIRROR HAS TWO FACES"
3	"THREE MEN AND A BABY"
4	"FANTASTIC FOUR"
5	"FIVE EASY PIECES"

SOLUTIONS: PAGE 284

Movie-Tac-Toe

Which row, column, or diagonal in the grid contains three films written by John Hughes?

FERRIS BUELLER'S DAY OFF	SIXTEEN CANDLES	THE KARATE KID
BACK TO THE FUTURE	WEIRD SCIENCE	PRETTY IN PINK
THE BREAKFAST CLUB	FAST TIMES AT RIDGEMONT HIGH	VACATION

SOLUTIONS: PAGE 284

Quick Quiz

Timothy Dalton's film debut was in what movie starring Katharine Hepburn?

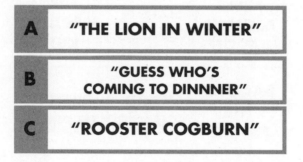

A "THE LION IN WINTER"

B "GUESS WHO'S COMING TO DINNNER"

C "ROOSTER COGBURN"

SOLUTIONS: PAGE 284

Film Strips

The crisscross below contains all of the words from a popular movie title. Add letters to contruct the words an discover the title.

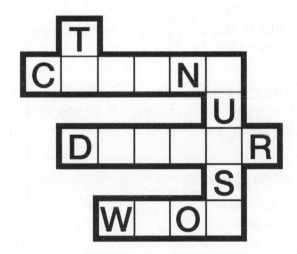

SOLUTIONS: PAGE 284

Movie-Tac-Toe

Which row, column, or diagonal in the grid contains three films that each had at least two sequels?

FERRIS BUELLER'S DAY OFF	PROBLEM CHILD	THE GODFATHER
BACK TO THE FUTURE	ST. ELMO'S FIRE	ROCKY
THE KARATE KID	AMERICAN GRAFFITI	JAWS

SOLUTIONS: PAGE 284

The Envelope, Please

The envelope below contains information about a prizewinning actor, movie, or both. All clues have been replaced with initials. Using the clues shown, can you determine what each set of initials stands for?

BEST ACTRESS WINNER:

J.A. *in*
"M.P."

SOLUTIONS: PAGE 284

Movie-Tac-Toe

Which row, column, or diagonal in the grid contains three films starring Morgan Freeman?

COURAGE UNDER FIRE	DRIVING MISS DAISY	INSIDE MAN
AMISTAD	THE SHAWSHANK REDEMPTION	PULP FICTION
THE SUM OF ALL FEARS	BRUCE ALMIGHTY	GLADIATOR

SOLUTIONS: PAGE 284

Script Tease

Fill in the word missing from each movie quote, then rearrange the first letters of the filled-in words to spell a 5-letter movie title.

1. "Say _____ to my little friend."
   —**"SCARFACE"**

2. "We're _____ to see the wizard..."
   —**"THE WIZARD OF OZ"**

3. "You _____ to me?" —**"TAXI DRIVER"**

4. "Of all the _____ joints in all the towns in all the world, she walks into mine."
   —**"CASABLANCA"**

5. "I feel the need, the need for _____!"
   —**"TOP GUN"**

Movie Title: ☐ ☐ ☐ ☐ ☐

SOLUTIONS: PAGE 284

The Envelope, Please

The envelope below contains information about a prizewinning actor, movie, or both. All clues have been replaced with initials. Using the clues shown, can you determine what each set of initials stands for?

BEST PICTURE WINNER:

"O.F.O.T.C.N."

Quick Quiz

What film's title theme reached the #1 position on the Billboard Hot 100?

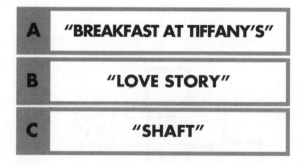

A "BREAKFAST AT TIFFANY'S"

B "LOVE STORY"

C "SHAFT"

SOLUTIONS: PAGE 284

Film Strips

The crisscross below contains all of the words from a popular movie title. Can you reconstruct the words and discover the title?

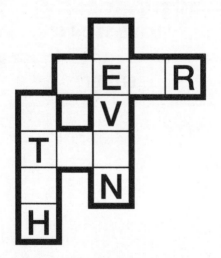

Movie Teaser

Rearrange the letters in the words below to spell the 2-word title of a popular 1992 movie.

RESIST CAT

SOLUTIONS: PAGE 284

Quick Quiz

In "The Shawshank Redemption," Tim Robbins' character Andy Dufresne had a poster of which screen queen on his prison cell wall?

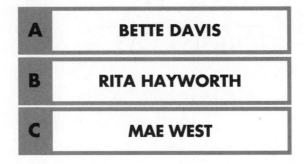

A	BETTE DAVIS
B	RITA HAYWORTH
C	MAE WEST

SOLUTIONS: PAGE 284

Order Please

Put these movies in order of their release, starting with the earliest.

1 "FOUR WEDDINGS AND A FUNERAL"

2 "WEDDING CRASHERS"

3 "MY BIG FAT GREEK WEDDING"

4 "THE WEDDING SINGER"

5 "MY BEST FRIEND'S WEDDING"

SOLUTIONS: PAGE 284

The Envelope, Please

The envelope below contains information about a prizewinning actor, movie, or both. All clues have been replaced with initials. Using the clues shown, can you determine what each set of initials stands for?

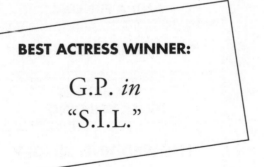

BEST ACTRESS WINNER:

G.P. *in*
"S.I.L."

Film Strips

The crisscross below contains all of the words from a popular movie title. Can you reconstruct the words and discover the title?

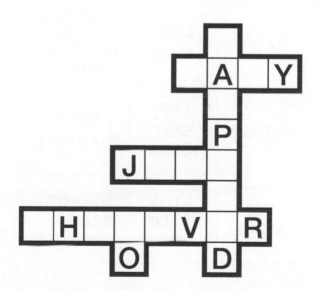

SOLUTIONS: PAGE 284

Movie-Tac-Toe

Which row, column, or diagonal in the grid contains three films starring Jack Nicholson?

JAWS	RAIN MAN	ONE FLEW OVER THE CUCKOO'S NEST
NETWORK	FIVE EASY PIECES	THE SHINING
THE STING	A FEW GOOD MEN	TERMS OF ENDEAR-MENT

SOLUTIONS: PAGE 284

Quick Quiz

What Brad Pitt film that's nearly 3 hours long was based on a 1922 short story by F. Scott Fitzgerald?

A	"FIGHT CLUB"
B	"SEVEN YEARS IN TIBET"
C	"THE CURIOUS CASE OF BENJAMIN BUTTON"

SOLUTIONS: PAGE 284

Match Game

Match the movies (left column) with the sports they feature prominently (right column).

1. "Bend It Like Beckham"
2. "The Big Lebowski"
3. "Bring It On"
4. "Bull Durham"
5. "Friday Night Lights"
6. "Happy Gilmore"
7. "Mystery, Alaska"
8. "Raging Bull"
9. "Secretariat"
10. "Teen Wolf"

A. Baseball
B. Basketball
C. Bowling
D. Boxing
E. Cheerleading
F. Football
G. Golf
H. Hockey
I. Horseracing
J. Soccer

SOLUTIONS: PAGE 284

The Envelope, Please

The envelope below contains information about a prizewinning actor, movie, or both. All clues have been replaced with initials. Using the clues shown, can you determine what each set of initials stands for?

BEST ACTRESS WINNER:

E.T. *in*
"W.A.O.V.W."

Movie-Tac-Toe

Which row, column, or diagonal in the grid contains three films starring Jim Carrey?

THE BIG LEBOWSKI	THE CABLE GUY	LIAR LIAR
STAND BY ME	A BEAUTIFUL MIND	PULP FICTION
THE TRUMAN SHOW	DUMB & DUMBER	THE MASK

SOLUTIONS: PAGE 284

Quick Quiz

In 1999, Cate Blanchett and Judi Dench were Best Actress nominees for playing the same character in different films. What character was it?

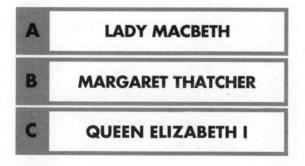

A   LADY MACBETH

B   MARGARET THATCHER

C   QUEEN ELIZABETH I

SOLUTIONS: PAGE 284

Order Please

What's shakin', Bacon? Put these Kevin Bacon films in order of their release, starting with the earliest.

1	"A FEW GOOD MEN"
2	"ANIMAL HOUSE"
3	"FOOTLOOSE"
4	"MYSTIC RIVER"
5	"SLEEPERS"

SOLUTIONS: PAGE 285

Hollywood Connections

The name is spelled in the grid by starting on the dot of the first letter and drawing a line from letter one to letter two, letter two to letter three, and so on, until the entire answer is spelled out.

Can you determine the answer?

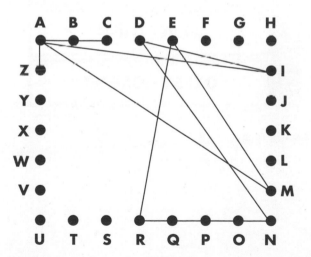

Quick Quiz

Jamie Lee-Curtis is the daughter of Tony Curtis and what legendary actress?

A	**VIVIEN LEIGH**
B	**JANET LEIGH**
C	**GYPSY ROSE LEE**

SOLUTIONS: PAGE 285

Remake My Day

Same title, different cast.
Can you identify the movie?

ORIGINAL CAST

RICKI LAKE
DIVINE

REMAKE CAST

NIKKI BLONSKY
JOHN TRAVOLTA

SOLUTIONS: PAGE 285

Fiction or non-?

True or False?

Brad Pitt and Will Smith
both turned down
the role of Neo in
"The Matrix" trilogy.

Movie Teaser

Rearrange the letters in the words below to spell the 2-word title of a popular 1957 movie.

LEERY DOLL

The Envelope, Please

The envelope below contains information about a prizewinning actor, movie, or both. All clues have been replaced with initials. Using the clues shown, can you determine what each set of initials stands for?

BEST DIRECTOR WINNER:

S.S. *for*
"S.P.R."

SOLUTIONS: PAGE 285

True or False?

Studies show that a woman who wins a Best Actress award is twice as likely to divorce her husband than a Best Actress nominee who doesn't win the award.

SOLUTIONS: PAGE 285

Quick Quiz

Fava beans and Chianti, anyone? What movie bad guy did the American Film Institute name the #1 movie villain of all time?

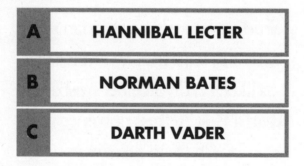

A HANNIBAL LECTER

B NORMAN BATES

C DARTH VADER

SOLUTIONS: PAGE 285

Remake My Day

Same title, different cast.
Can you identify the movie?

ORIGINAL CAST

ANTHONY PERKINS
JANET LEIGH

REMAKE CAST

VINCE VAUGHN
ANNE HECHE

SOLUTIONS: PAGE 285

Order Please

Put these films in order of their release, starting with the earliest.

1	"BORN ON THE FOURTH OF JULY"
2	"COMING TO AMERICA"
3	"INDEPENDENCE DAY"
4	"PATRIOT GAMES"
5	"STARS AND STRIPES FOREVER"

SOLUTIONS: PAGE 285

Movie-Tac-Toe

Which row, column, or diagonal in the grid contains three films released in 1994?

GHOST	FORREST GUMP	WHEN HARRY MET SALLY
HOME ALONE	SPEED	PRETTY WOMAN
THE LITTLE MERMAID	THE LION KING	DUMB AND DUMBER

SOLUTIONS: PAGE 285

Quick Quiz

Which movie studio with a roaring lion in its opening credits was founded in the Roaring Twenties?

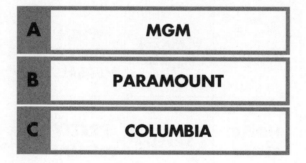

A	MGM
B	PARAMOUNT
C	COLUMBIA

SOLUTIONS: PAGE 285

Movie Teaser

Rearrange the letters in the words below to spell the 2-word title of a popular 1989 movie.

CUBE CLUNK

Movie-Tac-Toe

Which row, column, or diagonal in the grid contains three films starring Jennifer Aniston?

SIX DAYS SEVEN NIGHTS	MEET THE FOCKERS	THE BREAK-UP
VALENTINE'S DAY	RUMOR HAS IT	OFFICE SPACE
SCREAM	MARLEY & ME	BRUCE ALMIGHTY

SOLUTIONS: PAGE 285

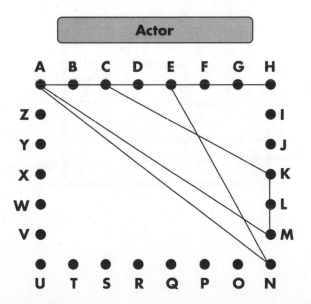

Hollywood Connections

The name is spelled in the grid by starting on the dot of the first letter and drawing a line from letter one to letter two, letter two to letter three, and so on, until the entire answer is spelled out.

Can you determine the answer?

Actor

A B C D E F G H
Z
Y
X K
W L
V M
U T S R Q P O N

SOLUTIONS: PAGE 285

Film Strips

The crisscross below contains all of the words from a popular movie title. Can you reconstruct the words and discover the title?

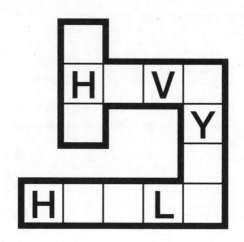

Movie Teaser

Rearrange the letters in the words below to spell the 2-word title of a popular 1990 movie.

LOCAL RATTLE

Quick Quiz

In "Misery," Annie Wilkes' pet Misery is what type of animal?

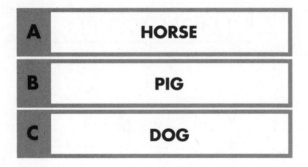

A	HORSE
B	PIG
C	DOG

SOLUTIONS: PAGE 285

Movie Teaser

Rearrange the letters in the words below to spell the 2-word title of a popular 1973 movie.

CHOIR SEXTET

SOLUTIONS: PAGE 285

Hollywood Connections

The name is spelled in the grid by starting on the dot of the first letter and drawing a line from letter one to letter two, letter two to letter three, and so on, until the entire answer is spelled out.

Can you determine the answer?

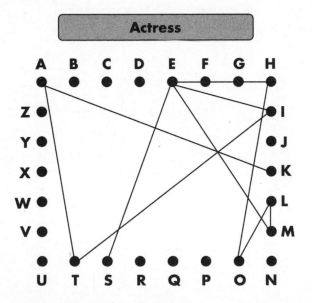

Actress

Order Please

Put these National Lampoon movies in order of their release, starting with the earliest.

1	**"CLASS REUNION"**
2	**"ANIMAL HOUSE"**
3	**"VAN WILDER"**
4	**"BARELY LEGAL"**
5	**"VACATION"**

SOLUTIONS: PAGE 285

Quick Quiz

Which TV show was inspired by a movie that was adapted from a novel?

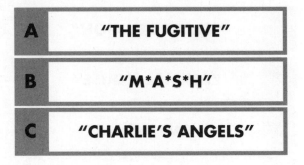

A	"THE FUGITIVE"
B	"M*A*S*H"
C	"CHARLIE'S ANGELS"

SOLUTIONS: PAGE 285

The Envelope, Please

The envelope below contains information about a prizewinning actor, movie, or both. All clues have been replaced with initials. Using the clues shown, can you determine what each set of initials stands for?

BEST ORIGINAL SONG WINNER:

"M.R." *from*
"B.A.T."

SOLUTIONS: PAGE 285

Hollywood Connections

The name is spelled in the grid by starting on the dot of the first letter and drawing a line from letter one to letter two, letter two to letter three, and so on, until the entire answer is spelled out.

Can you determine the answer?

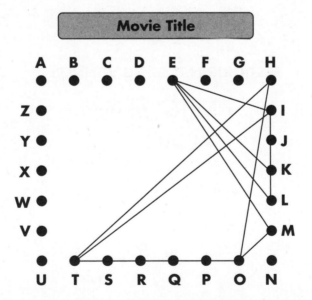

Movie Title

What's My Line?

Of Elizabeth Taylor's seven husbands, which was the only one she married and divorced twice?

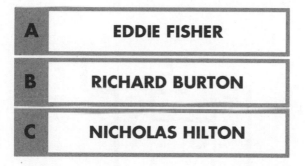

A	EDDIE FISHER
B	RICHARD BURTON
C	NICHOLAS HILTON

SOLUTIONS: PAGE 285

Film Strips

The crisscross below contains all of the words from a popular movie title. Can you reconstruct the words and discover the title?

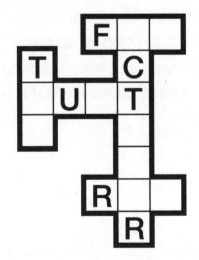

SOLUTIONS. PAGE 285

Script Tease

Fill in the word missing from each movie quote, then rearrange the first letters of the filled-in words to spell a 5-letter movie title.

1. "Every time a bell rings, an _____ gets his wings." —**"It's a Wonderful Life"**

2. "I love the smell of _____ in the morning." —**"Apocalypse Now"**

3. "I'll get you my pretty and your _____ dog, too?" —**"The Wizard of Oz"**

4. "A _____. Shaken, not stirred." —**"Goldfinger"**

5. "Round up the _____ suspects." —**"Casablanca"**

Movie Title: ☐☐☐☐☐

SOLUTIONS: PAGE 285

In "The Godfather," what did Marlon Brando stuff into his mouth to develop his distinctive mobster voice?

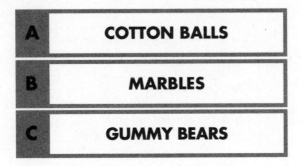

A	COTTON BALLS
B	MARBLES
C	GUMMY BEARS

Film Strips

The crisscross below contains all of the words from a popular movie title. Can you reconstruct the words and discover the title?

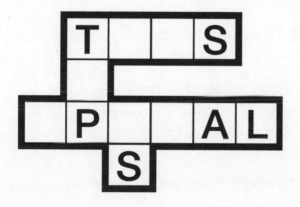

SOLUTIONS: PAGE 285

The Envelope, Please

The envelope below contains information about a prizewinning actor, movie, or both. All clues have been replaced with initials. Using the clues shown, can you determine what each set of initials stands for?

BEST PICTURE WINNER:

"K.V.K."

Quick Quiz

Which actor did not take a break from acting to serve in World War II?

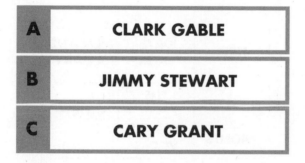

A   CLARK GABLE

B   JIMMY STEWART

C   CARY GRANT

SOLUTIONS: PAGE 285

Movie-Tac-Toe

Fill in the number missing from each movie title in the grid below, then find the row, column, or diagonal whose numbers total is 100.

___ HRS.	___ DAYS LATER	___ MEN AND A BABY
SIX DAYS ___ NIGHTS	THE ___-YEAR-OLD VIRGIN	CATCH- ___
THE ___ YEAR ITCH	___ MILE	___ ANGRY MEN

SOLUTIONS: PAGE 285

Movie Teaser

Rearrange the letters in the words below to spell the 2-word title of a popular 1993 movie.

DOUGHY DRAGON

SOLUTIONS: PAGE 285

The Envelope, Please

The envelope below contains information about a prizewinning actor, movie, or both. All clues have been replaced with initials. Using the clues shown, can you determine what each set of initials stands for?

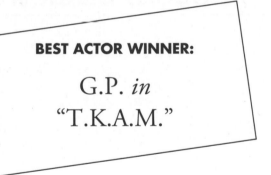

BEST ACTOR WINNER:

G.P. *in*
"T.K.A.M."

Quick Quiz

In "The Breakfast Club," which actor's character attended Saturday detention for lack of anything better to do?

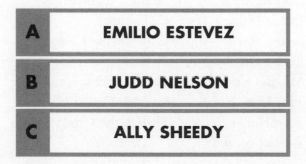

A EMILIO ESTEVEZ

B JUDD NELSON

C ALLY SHEEDY

SOLUTIONS: PAGE 285

Match Game

Match each actor with the character he or she voiced in the "Toy Story" movies.

1. Annie Potts
2. Don Rickles
3. Estelle Harris
4. Joan Cusack
5. John Raztenberger
6. Michael Keaton
7. Tim Allen
8. Tom Hanks
9. Wallace Shawn

A. Bo Peep
B. Buzz Lightyear
C. Hamm
D. Jessie the Cowgirl
E. Ken
F. Mr. Potato Head
G. Mrs. Potato Head
H. Rex the Green Dinosaur
I. Woody

SOLUTIONS: PAGE 285

Movie Teaser

Rearrange the letters in the words below to
spell the 2-word title of a popular 1973 movie.

STOLEN ENERGY

Order Please

Put these actors in order of their birth, starting with the earliest.

1	**DENZEL WASHINGTON**
2	**MARILYN MONROE**
3	**LIV TYLER**
4	**HUGH GRANT**
5	**CYNTHIA NIXON**

SOLUTIONS: PAGE 285

Movie Teaser

Rearrange the letters in the words below to spell the 2-word title of a popular 2005 movie.

PHANTOM TIC

Quick Quiz

In 1998, Eddie Murphy played "The Nutty Professor," a role originally played by what actor in 1963?

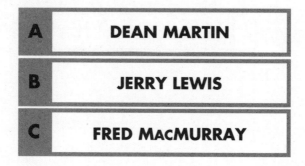

A   DEAN MARTIN

B   JERRY LEWIS

C   FRED MacMURRAY

SOLUTIONS: PAGE 286

Order Please

Put these actors in the order they portrayed James Bond, starting with the earliest.

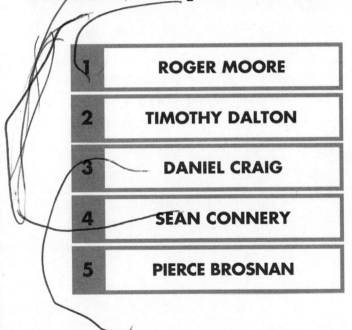

1	**ROGER MOORE**
2	**TIMOTHY DALTON**
3	**DANIEL CRAIG**
4	**SEAN CONNERY**
5	**PIERCE BROSNAN**

SOLUTIONS: PAGE 286

Movie Teaser

Rearrange the letters in the words below to spell the 2-word title of a popular 1984 movie.

> PURER PLAIN

Hollywood Connections

The name is spelled in the grid by starting on the dot of the first letter and drawing a line from letter one to letter two, letter two to letter three, and so on, until the entire answer is spelled out.

Can you determine the answer?

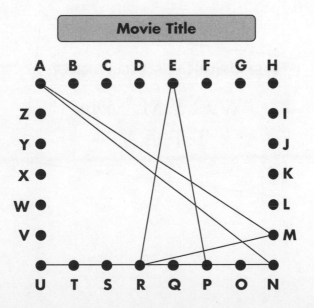

Movie Title

SOLUTIONS: PAGE 286

The Envelope, Please

The envelope below contains information about a prizewinning actor, movie, or both. All clues have been replaced with initials. Using the clues shown, can you determine what each set of initials stands for?

BEST ORIGINAL SONG WINNER:

"W.O.Y.M." *from* "T.T.C.A."

SOLUTIONS: PAGE 286

Order Please

Put these David Lynch films in order of their release, starting with the earliest.

1	"BLUE VELVET"
2	"THE ELEPHANT MAN"
3	"ERASERHEAD"
4	"MULHOLLAND DR."
5	"TWIN PEAKS: FIRE WALK WITH ME"

SOLUTIONS: PAGE 286

Quick Quiz

Which film featured Elizabeth Taylor but not Richard Burton?

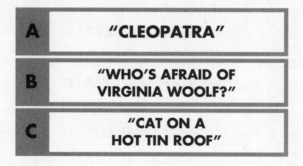

A   "CLEOPATRA"

B   "WHO'S AFRAID OF VIRGINIA WOOLF?"

C   "CAT ON A HOT TIN ROOF"

SOLUTIONS: PAGE 286

The List

Five of the following ten James Bond movies starred Sean Connery. Can you pick them out?

_____ "Goldfinger"

_____ "Licence to Kill"

_____ "You Only Live Twice"

_____ "From Russia With Love"

_____ "The Spy Who Loved Me"

_____ "Live and Let Die"

_____ "Moonraker"

_____ "Dr. No"

_____ "GoldenEye"

_____ "Diamonds Are Forever"

SOLUTIONS: PAGE 286

The Envelope, Please

The envelope below contains information about a prizewinning actor, movie, or both. All clues have been replaced with initials. Using the clues shown, can you determine what each set of initials stands for?

BEST ACTOR WINNER:

R.D.N. *in*
"R.B."

SOLUTIONS: PAGE 286

Quick Quiz

Which film's soundtrack includes the tracks "Fratelli Chase," "Map and Willie," and "Waterslide and Galleon"?

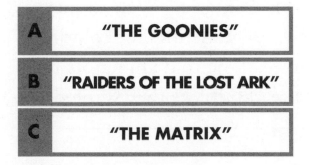

A "THE GOONIES"

B "RAIDERS OF THE LOST ARK"

C "THE MATRIX"

SOLUTIONS: PAGE 286

True or False?

For "Fantasia," Walt Disney gave no guidelines for coloring; instead, he told animators to use any colors they wanted.

Movie-Tac-Toe

Which row, column, or diagonal in the grid contains three actresses who've won two Best Actress awards?

JODIE FOSTER	**JANE FONDA**	**BETTE DAVIS**
ELIZABETH TAYLOR	**JULIE ANDREWS**	**SALLY FIELD**
JESSICA TANDY	**FAYE DUNAWAY**	**BARBRA STREISAND**

SOLUTIONS: PAGE 286

Quick Quiz

In "Field of Dreams," what actor played baseball legend Shoeless Joe Jackson?

A	**KEVIN COSTNER**
B	**VAL KILMER**
C	**RAY LIOTTA**

SOLUTIONS: PAGE 286

Hollywood Connections

The name is spelled in the grid by starting on the dot of the first letter and drawing a line from letter one to letter two, letter two to letter three, and so on, until the entire answer is spelled out.

Can you determine the answer?

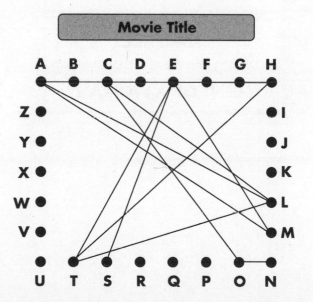

Movie Title

SOLUTIONS: PAGE 286

Quick Quiz

Al Pacino won a Best Actor Oscar for which film?

A	"THE GODFATHER"
B	"SCARFACE"
C	"SCENT OF A WOMAN"

SOLUTIONS: PAGE 286

Film Strips

The crisscross below contains all of the words from a popular movie title. Can you reconstruct the words and discover the title?

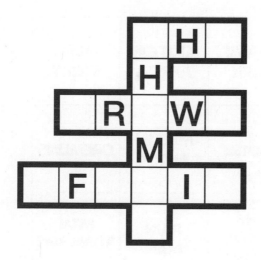

SOLUTIONS: PAGE 286

Movie-Tac-Toe

Which row, column, or diagonal in the grid contains three films released in the 1990s?

JURASSIC PARK	**OUT OF AFRICA**	**TOY STORY**
TOOTSIE	**MEN IN BLACK**	**GREMLINS**
THE SIXTH SENSE	**RAIN MAN**	**FATAL ATTRACTION**

SOLUTIONS: PAGE 286

Order Please

Put these actors in order of their birth, starting with the earliest.

1	**TOM BOSLEY**
2	**TOM CRUISE**
3	**TOM HANKS**
4	**TOM SELLECK**
5	**TOM SKERRITT**

SOLUTIONS: PAGE 286

Film Strips

The crisscross below contains all of the words from a popular movie title. Can you reconstruct the words and discover the title?

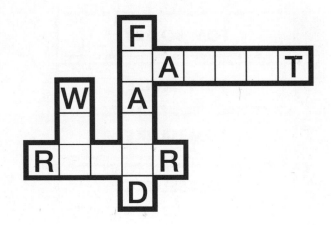

SOLUTIONS: PAGE 286

Quick Quiz

What movie did Ronald Reagan quote in his 1986 State of the Union speech when he said, "Where we're going, we don't need roads"?

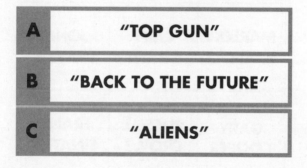

A   "TOP GUN"

B   "BACK TO THE FUTURE"

C   "ALIENS"

SOLUTIONS: PAGE 286

Movie-Tac-Toe

Which row, column, or diagonal in the grid contains three actors who have won two Best Actor awards?

MARLON BRANDO	CARY GRANT	JOHN WAYNE
GARY COOPER	RUSSELL CROWE	FRANK SINATRA
TOM HANKS	SEAN PENN	DUSTIN HOFFMAN

Film Strips

The crisscross below contains all of the words from a popular movie title. Can you reconstruct the words and discover the title?

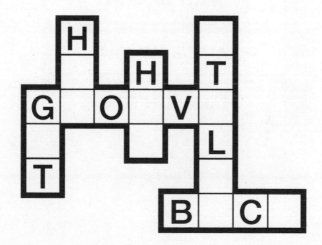

SOLUTIONS: PAGE 286

Quick Quiz

Which actor has not played protagonist Jack Ryan in a film based on a Tom Clancy novel?

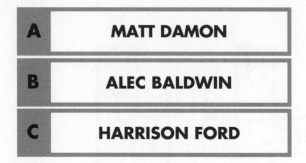

A	MATT DAMON
B	ALEC BALDWIN
C	HARRISON FORD

SOLUTIONS: PAGE 286

The name is spelled in the grid by starting on the dot of the first letter and drawing a line from letter one to letter two, letter two to letter three, and so on, until the entire answer is spelled out.

Can you determine the answer?

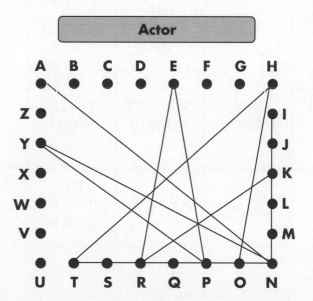

Actor

Movie-Tac-Toe

Which row, column, or diagonal in the grid contains titles of three films starring Drew Barrymore?

E.T.	THE BREAK UP	SCREAM
BIG DADDY	CHARLIE'S ANGELS	FEVER PITCH
OFFICE SPACE	AVATAR	THE WEDDING SINGER

SOLUTIONS: PAGE 286

Movie Teaser

Rearrange the letters in the words below to spell the 2-word title of a popular 1983 movie.

AVIATES LYING

SOLUTIONS: PAGE 286

The Envelope, Please

The envelope below contains information about a prizewinning actor, movie, or both. All clues have been replaced with initials. Using the clues shown, can you determine what each set of initials stands for?

BEST ACTOR WINNER:

M.B. *in*
"O.T.W."

Quick Quiz

In "Back to the Future," what does Lea Thompson assume Michael J. Fox's name is when she sees his underwear?

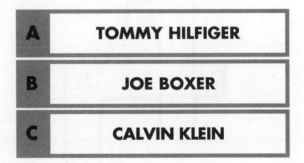

A	**TOMMY HILFIGER**
B	**JOE BOXER**
C	**CALVIN KLEIN**

SOLUTIONS: PAGE 286

Film Strips

The crisscross below contains all of the words from a popular movie title. Can you reconstruct the words and discover the title?

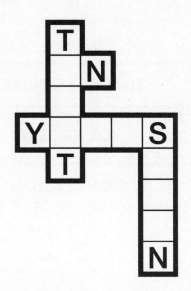

SOLUTIONS: PAGE 286

Quick Quiz

In a true case of role reversal, "Erin Brockovich" featured a cameo by the real-life Erin Brockovich —as a waitress named what?

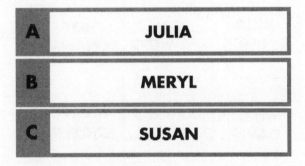

A	**JULIA**
B	**MERYL**
C	**SUSAN**

SOLUTIONS: PAGE 286

Movie-Tac-Toe

Which row, column, or diagonal in the grid contains three actresses who've been nominated more than 10 times for Best Actress?

JULIA ROBERTS	JOAN CRAWFORD	FAYE DUNAWAY
BETTE DAVIS	KATHARINE HEPBURN	MERYL STREEP
ELIZABETH TAYLOR	JODIE FOSTER	SUSAN SARANDON

SOLUTIONS: PAGE 286

The Envelope, Please

The envelope below contains information about a prizewinning actor, movie, or both. All clues have been replaced with initials. Using the clues shown, can you determine what each set of initials stands for?

BEST ACTOR WINNER:

A.P. *in*
"S.O.A.W."

SOLUTIONS: PAGE 286

True or False?

Johnny Carson opened one of his annual anniversary specials with a clip from "The Shining"—Jack Nicholson saying "Here's Johnny!"

Order Please

Put these songs in the order they won Best Original Song, starting with the earliest.

1	"FAME"
2	"(I'VE HAD) THE TIME OF MY LIFE"
3	"TAKE MY BREATH AWAY"
4	"THE WAY WE WERE"
5	"FLASHDANCE... WHAT A FEELING"

SOLUTIONS: PAGE 286

The Envelope, Please

The envelope below contains information about a prizewinning actor, movie, or both. All clues have been replaced with initials. Using the clues shown, can you determine what each set of initials stands for?

BEST ACTRESS WINNER:

S.S. *in*
"D.M.W."

SOLUTIONS: PAGE 286

Movie Teaser

Rearrange the letters in the words below to spell the 2-word title of a popular 1994 movie.

MOOD SHAPER

SOLUTIONS: PAGE 286

Film Strips

The crisscross below contains all of the words from a popular movie title. Can you reconstruct the words and discover the title?

SOLUTIONS: PAGE 286

Script Tease

Fill in the word missing from each movie quote, then rearrange the first letters of the filled-in words to spell a 5-letter movie title.

1. "Made it, Ma! _____ of the world!"
   —**"WHITE HEAT"**

2. "Mrs. _____, you're trying to seduce me."
   —**"THE GRADUATE"**

3. "I'm your number _____ fan. There's nothing to worry about." —**"MISERY"**

4. "Go _____, make my day."
   —**"SUDDEN IMPACT"**

5. "You're gonna need a _____ boat."
   —**"JAWS"**

Movie Title: ☐ ☐ ☐ ☐ ☐

SOLUTIONS: PAGE 286

Quick Quiz

Finish this line from Casablanca:
"Louis, I think this is the beginning of a beautiful
_____ ."

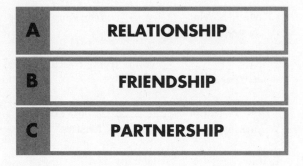

A   **RELATIONSHIP**

B   **FRIENDSHIP**

C   **PARTNERSHIP**

SOLUTIONS: PAGE 287

Hollywood Connections

The name is spelled in the grid by starting on the dot of the first letter and drawing a line from letter one to letter two, letter two to letter three, and so on, until the entire answer is spelled out.

Can you determine the answer?

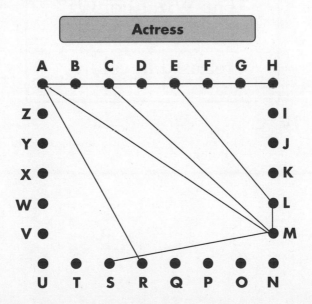

Actress

SOLUTIONS: PAGE 287

True or False?

"The Wizard of Oz"
was the first movie
released in color.

The Envelope, Please

The envelope below contains information about a prizewinning actor, movie, or both. All clues have been replaced with initials. Using the clues shown, can you determine what each set of initials stands for?

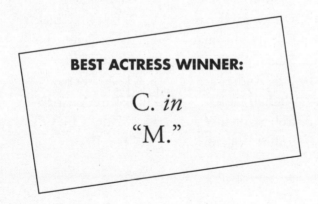

BEST ACTRESS WINNER:

C. *in*
"M."

Match Game

Match each actor with the movie in which he or she cross-dressed.

1. Barbra Streisand
2. Damon Wayans
3. Dustin Hoffman
4. Felicity Huffman
5. John Travolta
6. Julie Andrews
7. Nathan Lane
8. Rob Schneider
9. Robin Williams

A. "The Birdcage"
B. "Hairspray"
C. "The Hot Chick"
D. "Mrs. Doubtfire"
E. "Tootsie"
F. "Transamerica"
G. "Victor Victoria"
H. "White Chicks"
I. "Yentl"

SOLUTIONS: PAGE 287

Quick Quiz

Which thriller is based on a novel by Tom Clancy?

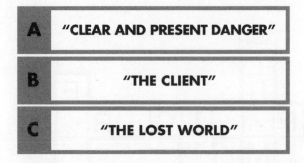

A	"CLEAR AND PRESENT DANGER"
B	"THE CLIENT"
C	"THE LOST WORLD"

SOLUTIONS: PAGE 287

Film Strips

The crisscross below contains all of the words from a popular movie title. Can you reconstruct the words and discover the title?

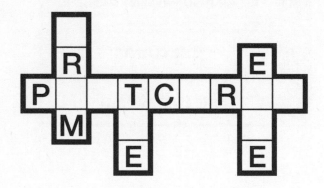

The Envelope, Please

The envelope below contains information about a prizewinning actor, movie, or both. All clues have been replaced with initials. Using the clues shown, can you determine what each set of initials stands for?

BEST ACTRESS WINNER:

R.W. *in*
"W.T.L."

SOLUTIONS: PAGE 287

Movie Teaser

Rearrange the letters in the words below to spell the 2-word title of a popular 1984 movie.

ENTICED LAXNESS

Order Please

Are you The King of movie trivia? Put these Elvis movies in order of their release, starting with the earliest.

1	"CHARRO!"
2	"BLUE HAWAII"
3	"VIVA LAS VEGAS"
4	"JAILHOUSE ROCK"
5	"G.I. BLUES"

SOLUTIONS: PAGE 287

Quick Quiz

What actor has gotten his kicks providing the voice for Donkey in all four "Shrek" films?

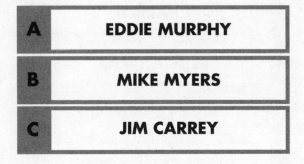

A	EDDIE MURPHY
B	MIKE MYERS
C	JIM CARREY

SOLUTIONS: PAGE 287

Movie Teaser

Rearrange the letters in the words below to spell the 2-word title of a popular 1997 movie.

OBOE SIGHTING

Movie-Tac-Toe

Which row, column, or diagonal in the grid contains three films released in the 1970s?

COMING TO AMERICA	THIS IS SPINAL TAP	ANNIE HALL
TO SIR, WITH LOVE	THE GRADUATE	BLAZING SADDLES
RISKY BUSINESS	TEEN WOLF	AMERICAN GRAFFITI

SOLUTIONS: PAGE 287

Movie Teaser

Rearrange the letters in the words below to spell the 2-word title of a popular 1987 movie.

| TREATS WELL |

Quick Quiz

While filming "Risky Business," Tom Cruise improvised the dance he did to what rock song?

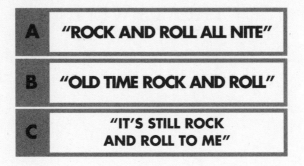

A "ROCK AND ROLL ALL NITE"

B "OLD TIME ROCK AND ROLL"

C "IT'S STILL ROCK AND ROLL TO ME"

SOLUTIONS: PAGE 287

Order Please

Put these Harry Potter films in order of their release, starting with the earliest. "Harry Potter and the..."

1 "...CHAMBER OF SECRETS"

2 "...GOBLET OF FIRE"

3 "...ORDER OF THE PHOENIX"

4 "...PRISONER OF AZKABAN"

5 "...SORCERER'S STONE"

SOLUTIONS: PAGE 287

The Envelope, Please

The envelope below contains information about a prizewinning actor, movie, or both. All clues have been replaced with initials. Using the clues shown, can you determine what each set of initials stands for?

BEST ACTRESS WINNER:

J.T. *in*
"D.M.D."

The List

Five of the following ten films were based on stories by Stephen King. Can you pick them out?

_____ "Stand By Me"
_____ "I Am Legend"
_____ "Hellraiser"
_____ "Dolores Claiborne"
_____ "Needful Things"
_____ "The Client"
_____ "Tremors"
_____ "Apt Pupil"
_____ "Poltergeist"
_____ "The Green Mile"

SOLUTIONS: PAGE 287

Film Strips

The crisscross below contains all of the words from a popular movie title. Can you reconstruct the words and discover the title?

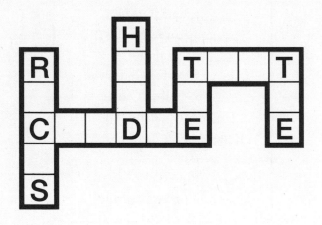

Remake My Day

Same title, different cast.
Can you identify the movie?

ORIGINAL CAST

SPENCER TRACY
ELIZABETH TAYLOR

REMAKE CAST

STEVE MARTIN
KIMBERLY WILLIAMS

SOLUTIONS: PAGE 287

Quick Quiz

In "A Christmas Story," what did Ralphie's Little Orphan Annie Decoder Ring tell him to drink?

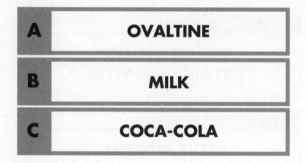

A OVALTINE

B MILK

C COCA-COLA

SOLUTIONS: PAGE 287

Movie Lines

Write a two-word movie title into the blanks to form a chain of three overlapping movie titles reading down. For example, given CURLY _____ _____ SHY, you'd write TOP GUN in the blanks to form CURLY TOP, TOP GUN, and GUN SHY.

DIE

_____

_____

MAN

Movie-Tac-Toe

Which row, column, or diagonal in the grid contains three films released in the 1960s?

REBEL WITHOUT A CAUSE	VALLEY OF THE DOLLS	SINGIN' IN THE RAIN
BYE BYE BIRDIE	JAILHOUSE ROCK	DR. NO
BONNIE AND CLYDE	WHO'S AFRAID OF VIRGINIA WOOLF?	THE SOUND OF MUSIC

SOLUTIONS: PAGE 287

Order Please

Put these films in the order they were released,
starting with the earliest.

1	"MARCH OF THE PENGUINS"
2	"ENCHANTED APRIL"
3	"WHAT DREAMS MAY COME"
4	"BORN ON THE FOURTH OF JULY"
5	"THE HUNT FOR RED OCTOBER"

SOLUTIONS: PAGE 287

Quick Quiz

Which couple is one of only two married couples in which both people won Best Acting awards?

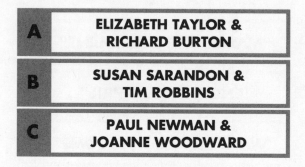

A   ELIZABETH TAYLOR & RICHARD BURTON

B   SUSAN SARANDON & TIM ROBBINS

C   PAUL NEWMAN & JOANNE WOODWARD

SOLUTIONS: PAGE 287

The Envelope, Please

The envelope below contains information about a prizewinning actor, movie, or both. All clues have been replaced with initials. Using the clues shown, can you determine what each set of initials stands for?

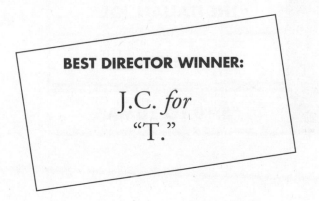

BEST DIRECTOR WINNER:

J.C. *for*

"T."

SOLUTIONS: PAGE 287

𝒬uick 𝒬uiz

What 2007 remake starred Michael Caine and Jude Law, with Jude Law playing the role Michael Caine played in the original 1972 film?

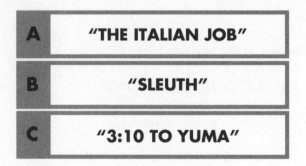

A — **"THE ITALIAN JOB"**

B — **"SLEUTH"**

C — **"3:10 TO YUMA"**

Film Strips

The crisscross below contains all of the words from a popular movie title. Can you reconstruct the words and discover the title?

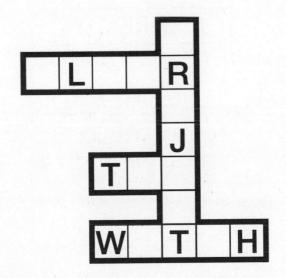

SOLUTIONS: PAGE 287

Movie Teaser

Rearrange the letters in the words below to spell the 2-word title of a popular 1969 movie.

RISE READY

Film Strips

The crisscross below contains all of the words
from a popular movie title. Can you reconstruct
the words and discover the title?

SOLUTIONS: PAGE 287

Quick Quiz

Which director is godfather to actress Drew Barrymore?

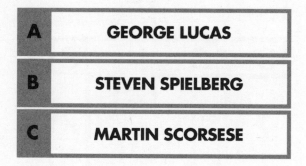

A   GEORGE LUCAS

B   STEVEN SPIELBERG

C   MARTIN SCORSESE

SOLUTIONS: PAGE 287

Film Strips

The crisscross below contains all of the words from a popular movie title. Can you reconstruct the words and discover the title?

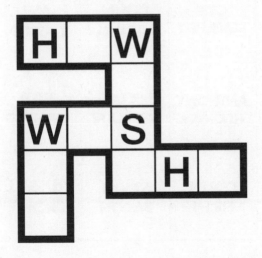

SOLUTIONS: PAGE 287

Movie-Tac-Toe

Which row, column, or diagonal in the grid contains three famous Australians?

CATE BLANCHETT	COLIN FARRELL	MEL GIBSON
ANTHONY HOPKINS	NICOLE KIDMAN	KATE WINSLET
COLIN FIRTH	KEVIN BACON	RUSSELL CROWE

SOLUTIONS: PAGE 287

Script Tease

Fill in the word missing from each movie quote, then rearrange the first letters of the filled-in words to spell a 5-letter movie title.

1. "My momma always said, 'Life was like a box of _____.'" —**"FORREST GUMP"**

2. "_____ kai-yay!" —**"DIE HARD"**

3. "_____ the pod bay doors, HAL." —**"2001: A SPACE ODYSSEY"**

4. "I have always depended on the _____ of strangers." —**"A STREETCAR NAMED DESIRE"**

5. "Does Barry Manilow know that you _____ his wardrobe?" —**"THE BREAKFAST CLUB"**

Movie Title: ☐ ☐ ☐ ☐ ☐

SOLUTIONS: PAGE 287

Quick Quiz

The "Magnum, P.I." episode "Legend of the Lost Art" was a nod to the fact that what actor was approached to play Indiana Jones?

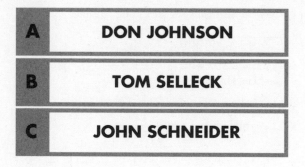

A   **DON JOHNSON**

B   **TOM SELLECK**

C   **JOHN SCHNEIDER**

SOLUTIONS: PAGE 287

The Envelope, Please

The envelope below contains information about a prizewinning actor, movie, or both. All clues have been replaced with initials. Using the clues shown, can you determine what each set of initials stands for?

BEST PICTURE WINNER:

"T.S.O.M."

Match Game

Match each director to the film that earned him or her a Best Director Oscar.

1. Ang Lee
2. Clint Eastwood
3. Danny Boyle
4. Kathryn Bigelow
5. Kevin Costner
6. Martin Scorsese
7. Mel Gibson
8. Oliver Stone
9. Robert Redford

A. "Braveheart"
B. "Brokeback Mountain"
C. "Dances With Wolves"
D. "The Departed"
E. "The Hurt Locker"
F. "Million Dollar Baby"
G. "Ordinary People"
H. "Platoon"
I. "Slumdog Millionaire"

SOLUTIONS: PAGE 287

Hollywood Connections

The name is spelled in the grid by starting on the dot of the first letter and drawing a line from letter one to letter two, letter two to letter three, and so on, until the entire answer is spelled out.

Can you determine the answer?

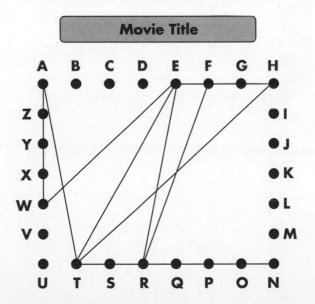

Movie Title

A B C D E F G H
Z Y X W V
U T S R Q P O N
I J K L M

SOLUTIONS: PAGE 287

Quick Quiz

Which film's lead actor has the same first name as the person he plays in the movie?

A	"PATTON"
B	"MILK"
C	"ALI"

SOLUTIONS: PAGE 288

The Envelope, Please

The envelope below contains information about a prizewinning actor, movie, or both. All clues have been replaced with initials. Using the clues shown, can you determine what each set of initials stands for?

BEST ACTRESS WINNER:

J.R. *in*
"E.B."

SOLUTIONS: PAGE 288

Movie Teaser

Rearrange the letters in the words below to spell the 3-word title of a popular 1950 movie.

LOVE TABLEAU

Fiction or non-?

> Oscar Hammerstein II is the only person named Oscar to win an Oscar.

SOLUTIONS: PAGE 288

Movie Teaser

Rearrange the letters in the words below to spell the 2-word title of a popular 1994 movie.

FROG STUMPER

Film Strips

The crisscross below contains all of the words from a popular movie title. Can you reconstruct the words and discover the title?

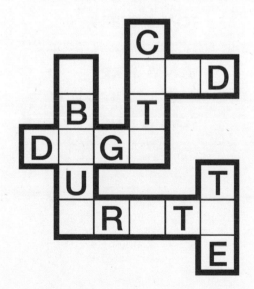

SOLUTIONS: PAGE 288

Quick Quiz

A film titled "Meet the Stillers" might feature what celebrity father and son who both have the last name Stiller?

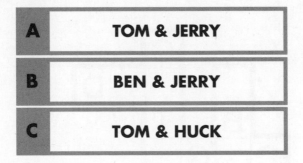

A TOM & JERRY

B BEN & JERRY

C TOM & HUCK

SOLUTIONS: PAGE 288

Order Please

Put these Michaels in order of their birth, starting with the earliest.

1	**MICHAEL CAINE**
2	**MICHAEL DOUGLAS**
3	**MICHAEL J. FOX**
4	**MICHAEL C. HALL**
5	**MICHAEL KEATON**

SOLUTIONS: PAGE 288

The Envelope, Please

The envelope below contains information about a prizewinning actor, movie, or both. All clues have been replaced with initials. Using the clues shown, can you determine what each set of initials stands for?

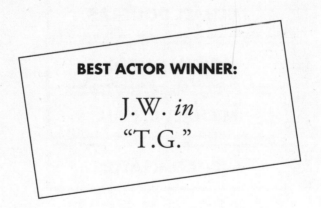

BEST ACTOR WINNER:

J.W. *in*
"T.G."

SOLUTIONS: PAGE 288

Film Strips

The crisscross below contains all of the words from a popular movie title. Can you reconstruct the words and discover the title?

SOLUTIONS: PAGE 288

Quick Quiz

On the first day filming "On Golden Pond," Katharine Hepburn presented Henry Fonda with a "lucky" hat that belonged to whom?

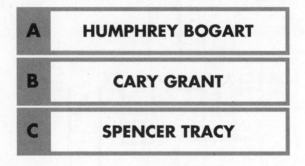

A	HUMPHREY BOGART
B	CARY GRANT
C	SPENCER TRACY

SOLUTIONS: PAGE 288

Remake My Day

Same title, different cast.
Can you identify the movie?

**JERRY LEWIS
STELLA STEVENS**

**EDDIE MURPHY
JADA PINKETT SMITH**

SOLUTIONS: PAGE 288

The name is spelled in the grid by starting on the dot of the first letter and drawing a line from letter one to letter two, letter two to letter three, and so on, until the entire answer is spelled out.

Can you determine the answer?

Actor

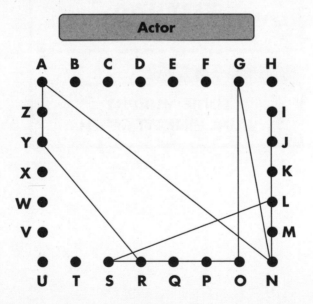

SOLUTIONS: PAGE 288

Released in 1991, what was the first animated film to be nominated for the Best Picture Oscar?

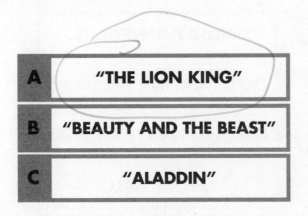

A "THE LION KING"

B "BEAUTY AND THE BEAST"

C "ALADDIN"

Order Please

Put these Woody Allen films in order of their release, starting with the earliest.

1	**MIGHTY APHRODITE**
2	**CRIMES AND MISDEMEANORS**
3	**HANNAH AND HER SISTERS**
4	**ANNIE HALL**
5	**MATCH POINT**

The Envelope, Please

The envelope below contains information about a prizewinning actor, movie, or both. All clues have been replaced with initials. Using the clues shown, can you determine what each set of initials stands for?

BEST ACTRESS WINNER:

D.K. *in*
"A.H."

The List

Four of the following nine Alfred Hitchcock films featured Jimmy Stewart. Can you pick them out?

_____ "North by Northwest"

_____ "The Man Who
        Knew Too Much"

_____ "Rear Window"

_____ "Psycho"

_____ "To Catch a Thief"

_____ "Vertigo"

_____ "The Birds"

_____ "Rope"

_____ "The Lady Vanishes"

SOLUTIONS: PAGE 288

Quick Quiz

In "The Big Lebowski," Jeff Bridges' character
'The Dude' had a fondness for what drink?

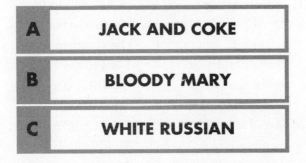

A   JACK AND COKE

B   BLOODY MARY

C   WHITE RUSSIAN

SOLUTIONS: PAGE 288

Match Game

Match each actor with the film in which he played the title role.

1. Adrian Brody
2. Arnold Schwarzenegger
3. Dustin Hoffman
4. Kevin Costner
5. Marlon Brando
6. Matt Damon
7. Paul Newman
8. Robert Redford
9. Tim Robbins

A. "The Bodyguard"
B. "The Godfather"
C. "The Graduate"
D. "The Hustler"
E. "The Informant"
F. "The Natural"
G. "The Pianist"
H. "The Player"
I. "The Terminator"

SOLUTIONS: PAGE 288

Movie-Tac-Toe

Which row, column, or diagonal in the grid contains titles of three films that premiered in the 2000s?

XXX	AMERICAN HISTORY X	OH, GOD!
O BROTHER, WHERE ARE THOU?	MALCOLM X	THE X FILES
X-MEN	OH! CALCUTTA!	MY SUPER EX-GIRLFRIEND

SOLUTIONS: PAGE 288

Order Please

Put these movies in order of their release, starting with the earliest.

1	"A CHRISTMAS STORY"
2	"HOW THE GRINCH STOLE CHRISTMAS" (Jim Carrey version)
3	"THE NIGHTMARE BEFORE CHRISTMAS"
4	"WHITE CHRISTMAS"
5	"CHRISTMAS VACATION"

SOLUTIONS: PAGE 288

Movie Teaser

Rearrange the letters in the words below to spell the 2-word title of a popular 1999 movie.

THIN TOLLING

SOLUTIONS: PAGE 288

Script Tease

Fill in the word missing from each movie quote, then rearrange the first letters of the filled-in words to spell a 5-letter movie title.

1. "You can't handle the _____!"
   —**"A FEW GOOD MEN"**

2. "I'm not gonna be _____, Dan."
   —**"FATAL ATTRACTION"**

3. "I coulda been a _____."
   —**"ON THE WATERFRONT"**

4. "As God is my witness, I'll never go _____ again." —**"GONE WITH THE WIND"**

5. "_____, we have a problem."
   —**"APOLLO 13"**

Movie Title: ☐☐☐☐☐

SOLUTIONS: PAGE 288

Hollywood Connections

The name is spelled in the grid by starting on the dot of the first letter and drawing a line from letter one to letter two, letter two to letter three, and so on, until the entire answer is spelled out.

Can you determine the answer?

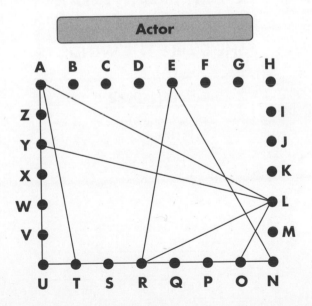

Actor

SOLUTIONS: PAGE 288

Quick Quiz

Which big-screen ballad was co-written by Patrick Swayze?

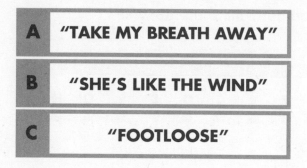

A "TAKE MY BREATH AWAY"

B "SHE'S LIKE THE WIND"

C "FOOTLOOSE"

SOLUTIONS: PAGE 288

Order Please

Put these Christopher Guest films in the order they were released, starting with the earliest.

1	"BEST IN SHOW"
2	"A MIGHTY WIND"
3	"THIS IS SPINAL TAP"
4	"WAITING FOR GUFFMAN"
5	"FOR YOUR CONSIDERATION"

SOLUTIONS: PAGE 288

Movie-Tac-Toe

Which row, column, or diagonal in the grid contains three Best Picture winners from the 1970s?

CHARIOTS OF FIRE	THE STING	PLATOON
MY FAIR LADY	ROCKY	BEN-HUR
ORDINARY PEOPLE	MIDNIGHT COWBOY	WEST SIDE STORY

SOLUTIONS: PAGE 288

The Envelope, Please

The envelope below contains information about a prizewinning actor, movie, or both. All clues have been replaced with initials. Using the clues shown, can you determine what each set of initials stands for?

BEST ORIGINAL SONG WINNER:

"T.M.B.A." *from*
"T.G."

SOLUTIONS: PAGE 288

Quick Quiz

Only two films have been nominated for a record 14 Academy Awards. "All About Eve," and what other film?

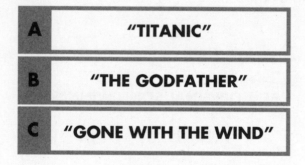

A	"TITANIC"
B	"THE GODFATHER"
C	"GONE WITH THE WIND"

SOLUTIONS: PAGE 288

Movie Teaser

Rearrange the letters in the words below to spell the 2-word title of a popular 1999 movie.

HAZE NASTILY

Quick Quiz

Which film was based on an unproduced play titled "Everybody Comes to Rick's"?

A	"GONE WITH THE WIND"
B	"CASABLANCA"
C	"IT'S A WONDERFUL LIFE"

SOLUTIONS: PAGE 288

Movie-Tac-Toe

Which row, column, or diagonal in the grid contains three movie musicals that won Best Picture?

WEST SIDE STORY	THE KING AND I	OKLAHOMA!
RENT	OLIVER!	MY FAIR LADY
THE SOUND OF MUSIC	THE PRODUCERS	CHICAGO

SOLUTIONS: PAGE 288

Quick Quiz

Which movie star spouses have the largest age difference between them?

A	**MICHAEL DOUGLAS & CATHERINE ZETA-JONES**
B	**DEMI MOORE & ASHTON KUTCHER**
C	**HARRISON FORD & CALISTA FLOCKHART**

1. I-G, 2-H, 3-F, 4-A, 5-J, 6-C, 7-B, 8-D, 9-I, 10-E.

2. I. RAIN, 2. ANYMORE, 3. GOES, 4. FRANKLY, 5. OUT. The first letters of these words can be rearranged to spell FARGO.

3. THE THOMAS CROWN AFFAIR.

4. Natalie Portman.

5. RAIDERS OF THE LOST ARK.

6. The rightmost column.

7. Alfred Hitchcock.

8. INFO MENDING can be rearranged to spell FINDING NEMO.

9. The middle column.

10. FALSE. He won for "On Golden Pond," his last movie.

11. Channing Tatum.

12. "Apocalypse Now," "The Fugitive," "Six Days Seven Nights," "Patriot Games," and "Air Force One".

13. The correct order is — 2 (12 nominations), 5 (5 nominations), 4 (4 nominations), I (3 nominations), 3 (2 nominations).

14. I. Orange, 2. Yellow, 3. Pink, 4. Black, 5. Green, 6. Blue, 7. White, 8. Brown, 9. Red.

15. I—G, 2—A, 3—D, 4—B, 5—H, 6—E, 7—C, 8—F.

16. I. REFUSE, 2. ELEMENTARY, 3. SORRY, 4. KANSAS, 5. HOME. The first letters of these words can be rearranged to spell SHREK.

17. TRUE GRIT.

18. THE WIZARD OF OZ.

19. THE GREAT TRAIN ROBBERY.

20. The diagonal from top right to bottom left.

21. ANSWERS: B: "The Bodyguard." Other top-selling soundtracks include "Saturday Night Fever" (15 million albums), "Purple Rain" (13 million), "Forrest Gump" (12 million), "Titanic" (11 million), and "Dirty Dancing" (11 million).

22. NASTY HAYING can be rearranged to spell SAY ANYTHING.

23. CLINT EASTWOOD for MILLION DOLLAR BABY.

24. TRUE. Dean appeared in "East of Eden," "Rebel Without a Cause," and "Giant."

25. B: Martin Sheen, father of Emilio Estevez and Charlie Sheen, who was born Carlos Estevez.

26. "Blood Simple," "Burn After Reading," "Fargo," "The Man Who Wasn't There," "Raising Arizona."

27. The correct order is: 4 (1995), 2 (2003), 3 (2004), 5 (2008), I (2009).

28. The diagonal from bottom left to top right.

29. HELEN HUNT in AS GOOD AS IT GETS.

30. LEAVING LAS VEGAS.

31. B: Vince Vaughn.

32. PENELOPE CRUZ.

33. NARROW WIDE can be rearranged to spell REAR WINDOW.

34. FAST TIMES AT RIDGEMONT HIGH.

35. THE MIDDLE ROW.

36. PALE POTENCY can be rearranged to spell PEYTON PLACE.

37. SISSY SPACEK in COAL MINER'S DAUGHTER.

38. TEMPT NORWAY can be rearranged to spell PRETTY WOMAN.

39. MONTY PYTHON AND THE HOLY GRAIL.

40. OLIVER STONE.

41. The correct order is: 5 (1989), 4 (1991), 1 (1992), 3 (1994), 2 (1995).

42. A: Barbra Streisand for "Funny Girl."

43. TRUE. The role went to Angelina Jolie.

44. The rightmost column.

45. B: "Fatal Attraction."

46. FALSE. Liza Minnelli is the daughter of Judy Garland.

47. MARRIED TO THE MOB.

48. The correct order is: 3 (1956), 2 (1963), 5 (1967), 4 (1970), 1 (1981).

49. The leftmost column.

50. MEAN ROAR can be rearranged to spell NORMA RAE

51. C: "Apocalypse Now." Nicolas Cage's uncle is Francis Ford Coppola.

52. THE DA VINCI CODE.

53. The diagonal from top left to bottom right.

54. 1—H, 2—J, 3—D, 4—A, 5—C, 6—F, 7—E, 8—G, 9—I, 10—B.

55. The correct order is: 5 (1982), 4 (1983), 3 (1985), 1 (2006), 2 (2009).

56. DUSTIN HOFFMAN in RAIN MAN.

57. A: "All About Steve."

58. 1. IF, 2. BABY, 3. BASEBALL, 4. ANOTHER, 5. MONEY. The first letters of these words can be rearranged to spell BAMBI.

59. ONE FLEW OVER THE CUCKOO'S NEST.

60. JOEL & ETHAN COEN for NO COUNTRY FOR OLD MEN.

61. The diagonal from top right to bottom left.

62. TRITE RUG can be rearranged to spell TRUE GRIT.

63. THE POSTMAN ALWAYS RINGS TWICE.

64. C: Reese's Pieces.

65. The correct order is: 4 (1980), 2 (1986), 5 (1987), 1 (2003), 3 (2010).

66. HUMPHREY BOGART in THE AFRICAN QUEEN.

67. B: Bob Hope.

68. The rightmost column.

69. SO OVERTLY can be rearranged to spell LOVE STORY.

70. A: "Citizen Kane." The film was booed because of its unflattering portrayal of William Randolph Hearst.

71. The movies that won Best Picture are "Gladiator," "Titanic," "Rocky," "Braveheart," and "Casablanca."

72. SINGIN' IN THE RAIN.

73. A: Gary Cooper

74. The top row.

75. B: "The Sound of Music." The songs are "The Sound of Music," "Do Re Mi," and "My Favorite Things.".

76. ANTHONY HOPKINS in THE SILENCE OF THE LAMBS.

77. SAVING PRIVATE RYAN.

78. CHARIOTS OF FIRE.

79. The correct order is: 2 (1983), 4 (1989), 3 (1993), 1 (1996), 5 (1998).

80. B: His lawyer. Spielberg's dog appeared in "Jaws"—as Roy Scheider's dog.

81. The diagonal from bottom left to top right.

82. 1. Seattle, 2. Las Vegas, 3. L.A., 4. St. Louis, 5. Miami, 6. Cairo, 7. Barcelona, 8. Yuma.

83. The diagonal from bottom left to top right.

84. SOME LIKE IT HOT.

85. A: Woody Allen.

86. HEATH LEDGER.

87. The diagonal from top left to bottom right.

88. DANCES WITH WOLVES.

89. SHIRLEY MACLAINE in TERMS OF ENDEARMENT.

90. ROMAN POPE can be rearranged to spell PAPER MOON.

91. 1—F, 2—B, 3—C, 4—I, 5—G, 6—A, 7—E, 8—D, 9—H.

92. The correct order is: 1 (1980), 5 (1992), 4 (1999), 2 (2000), 3 (2010).

93. THE TAKING OF PELHAM ONE TWO THREE.

94. C: Angelina Jolie.

95. The correct order is: 4 (1976), 1 (1981), 5 (1996), 3 (1998), 2 (2008).

96. VIVIEN LEIGH in A STREETCAR NAMED DESIRE.

97. The leftmost column.

98. CAPPED TIME can be rearranged to spell DEEP IMPACT.

99. A: Tom Hanks.

100. GENE HACKMAN in THE FRENCH CONNECTION.

101. GEORGE LUCAS.

102. B: Kate Hudson. Goldie Hawn is her mother.

103. C: "The Breakfast Club."

104. CANDID TRYING can be rearranged to spell DIRTY DANCING.

105. The correct order is: 5 (1970), 1 (1975), 3 (1987), 2 (1996), 4 (2005).

106. The diagonal from top left to bottom right.

107. A: "The Lion in Winter."

108. GUESS WHO'S COMING TO DINNER.

109. The rightmost column.

110. JULIE ANDREWS in MARY POPPINS.

111. The middle column..

112. 1. HELLO, 2. OFF, 3. TALKIN', 4. GIN, 5. SPEED. The first letters of these words can be rearranged to spell GHOST.

113. ONE FLEW OVER THE CUCKOO'S NEST.

114. C: "Shaft."

115. THE SEVEN YEAR ITCH.

116. RESIST CAT can be rearranged to spell SISTER ACT.

117. B: Rita Hayworth. "The Shawshank Redemption" was based on the Stephen King novella "Rita Hayworth and Shawshank Redemption."

118. The correct order is: 1 (1994), 5 (1997), 4 (1998), 3 (2002), 2 (2005).

119. GWYNETH PALTROW in SHAKESPEARE IN LOVE.

120. WHATEVER HAPPENED TO BABY JANE.

121. The rightmost column.

122. C: "The Curious Case of Benjamin Button."

123. 1—J, 2—C, 3—E, 4—A, 5—F, 6—G, 7—H, 8—D, 9—I, 10—B.

124. ELIZABETH TAYLOR in WHO'S AFRAID OF VIRGINIA WOOLF.

125. The bottom row.

126. C: Queen Elizabeth I. Cate Blanchett played her in "Elizabeth." Judi Dench played her in "Shakespeare In Love" and won.

127. The correct order is: 2 (1978), 3 (1984), 1 (1992), 5 (1996), 4 (2003).

128. CAMERON DIAZ.

129. B: Janet Leigh.

130. HAIRSPRAY.

131. TRUE.

132. LERRY DOLL can be rearranged to spell OLD YELLER.

133. STEVEN SPIELBERG for SAVING PRIVATE RYAN.

134. TRUE.

135. A: Hannibal Lecter.

136. PSYCHO.

137. The correct order is: 5 (1952), 2 (1988), 1 (1989), 4 (1992), 3 (1996).

138. The middle column.

139. A: MGM was founded in 1924.

140. CUBE CLUNK can be rearranged to spell UNCLE BUCK.

141. The rightmost column.

142. GENE HACKMAN.

143. THE HILLS HAVE EYES.

144. LOCAL RATTLE can be rearranged to spell TOTAL RECALL.

145. B: PIG.

146. CHOIR SEXTET can be rearranged to spell THE EXORCIST.

147. KATIE HOLMES.

148. The correct order is: 2 (1978), 1 (1982), 5 (1983), 3 (2002), 4 (2003).

149. B: "M*A*S*H." Richard Hooker's novel was released in 1968. In 1970, Robert Altman directed a film based on the novel. The TV series ran from 1972—77

150. MOON RIVER from BREAKFAST AT TIFFANY'S.

151. SOME LIKE IT HOT.

152. B: Richard Burton.

153. THE HUNT FOR RED OCTOBER.

154. 1. ANGEL, 2. NAPALM, 3. LITTLE, 4. MARTINI, 5. USUAL. The first letters of these words can be rearranged to spell MULAN.

155. B: Marbles.

156. THIS IS SPINAL TAP.

157. KRAMER VS. KRAMER.

158. C: Cary Grant.

159. Row by row, the titles are: 48 Hrs., 28 Days Later, Three Men and a Baby, Six Days Seven Nights, The 40-Year-Old Virgin, Catch-22, The Seven Year Itch, 8 Mile, 12 Angry Men. The diagonal from top left to bottom right (48 + 40 + 12) totals 100.

160. DOUGHY DRAGON can be rearranged to spell GROUNDHOG DAY.

161. GREGORY PECK in TO KILL A MOCKINGBIRD.

162. C: Ally Sheedy.

163. 1—A, 2—F, 3—G, 4—D, 5—C, 6—E, 7—B, 8—I, 9—H.

164. STOLEN ENERGY can be rearranged to spell SOYLENT GREEN.

165. THE CORRECT ORDER IS: 2 (1926), 1 (1954), 4 (1960), 5 (1966), 3 (1977).

166. PHANTOM TIC can be rearranged to spell MATCH POINT.

167. B: Jerry Lewis.

168. THE CORRECT ORDER IS: 4, 1, 2, 5, 3.

169. PURER PLAIN can be rearranged to spell PURPLE RAIN.

170. SUPERMAN.

171. WINDMILLS OF YOUR MIND from THE THOMAS CROWN AFFAIR.

172. The correct order is: 3 (1977), 2 (1980), 1 (1986), 5 (1992), 4 (2001).

173. C: "Cat on a Hot Tin Roof."

174. "Goldfinger," "You Only Live Twice," "From Russia With Love," "Dr. No," and "Diamonds Are Forever."

175. ROBERT DE NIRO in RAGING BULL.

176. A: "The Goonies."

177. TRUE

178. The top row. Other actresses in the grid who have won two Best Actress awards are Elizabeth Taylor and Sally Field.

179. C: Ray Liotta.

180. THE MALTESE FALCON.

181. C: "Scent of a Woman."

182. THE THOMAS CROWN AFFAIR.

183. The diagonal from bottom left to top right.

184. The correct order is: 1 (1927), 5 (1933), 4 (1945), 3 (1956), 2 (1962).

185. WHO FRAMED ROGER RABBIT.

186. B: "Back to the Future."

187. The bottom row. Other actors in the grid who have won two Best Actor awards are Marlon Brando and Gary Cooper.

188. HOW STELLA GOT HER GROOVE BACK.

189. A: Matt Damon.

190. ANTHONY PERKINS.

191. The diagonal from top left to bottom right.

192. AVIATES LYING can be rearranged to spell STAYING ALIVE.

193. MARLON BRANDO in ON THE WATERFRONT.

194. C: Calvin Klein.

195. SEVEN YEARS IN TIBET.

196. A: Julia. Julia Roberts played Erin Brockovich in the film.

197. The middle row. Bette Davis was nominated 11 times, Katharine Hepburn was nominated 12 times, and Meryl Streep has been nominated 13 times.

198. AL PACINO in SCENT OF A WOMAN.

199. TRUE. Jack Nicholson ad-libbed the famous line during filming of "The Shining."

200. ANSWERS: The correct order is: 4, 1, 5, 3, 2.

201. SUSAN SARANDON in DEAD MAN WALKING.

202. MOOD SHAPER can be rearranged to spell HOOP DREAMS.

203. LITTLE MISS SUNSHINE.

204. 1. TOP, 2. ROBINSON, 3. ONE, 4. AHEAD, 5. BIGGER. The first letters of these words can be rearranged to spell BORAT.